HEINEMANN
SECONDARY
HISTORY
PROJECT

MEDICINE THROUGH TIME

FOUNDATION EDITION

Fiona Reynoldson

Heinemann Educational Publishers

Halley Court, Jordan Hill, Oxford OX2 8EJ
Part of Harcourt Education
Heinemann is a registered trademark of
Harcourt Education Limited

Tel: 01865 888058 www.heinemann.co.uk

Teacher support material and activities for students are available for this title at www.heinemann.co.uk/medicine.

You will need to use a password to gain access to this material. The passwords are :

for material to support the *core edition* of this book : **core**
for material to support the *foundation edition* of this book : **foundation**

© Fiona Reynoldson 2002

Original illustrations © Harcourt Education Limited 2002

First published 2002

07 06
10 9 8 7 6 5 4

10-digit ISBN: 0 435308 40 8
13-digit ISBN: 978 0 435308 40 7

Designed by Ken Vail Graphic Design

Illustrated by Arthur Phillips

Printed in Italy by Printer Trento Srl

Cover design by The Wooden Ark Studio

Photographic acknowledgements

The authors and publisher would like to thank the following for permission to reproduce photographs:

Ancient Art and Architecture Collection: 1.1A, 5.3I; Ann Ronan Picture Library: 8.5I, 9.4Q; Antonia Reeve/Science Photo Library: 12.3O; Australian Aboriginal Cultures Gallery, South Australian Museum: 1.4E; Bibliotheque Nationale Paris: 7.4F, 13.1B; Bodleian Library: 9.1A; Bridgeman Art Library/Private Collection: 11.5O; Bridgeman Art Library: 2.2A; Bridgeman Art Library/Musee de L'Hotel Sandelin: 9.6 (1); Bridgeman Art Library/York City Art Gallery: 9.5T; British Library Reproductions: 8.4G, 8.6O; British Museum Library: 4.6I, 5.6 (2), 9.2G; BSIP, Edwige/Science Photo Library: 12.3N; C.M. Dixon: 3.1A, 3.2B, 4.1A, 5.3H; Cambridge University Library: 8.2D; Centre for the Study of Cartoons, University of Kent: 13.4X; Chester Beatty Library, Dublin/Cumulus: 7.2A; Coo.ee Historical Picture Archive: 1.4F; Corbis Bettman/UPI: 12.2L; Count Robert Begouen, Musee Pujol, France: 1.2C; E.T. Archive: 4.6K, 12.1A; Francesca Countway Library: 12.1C; Frank Graham: 5.3G; Hildesheim Museum: 2.3C; Hulton Deutsch Collection: 11.3J, 12.3 (p.113), 12.5 (p.119 bottom), 13.2 (p.126); Hulton-Deutsch Collection/Corbis: 13.4 (p.135); Imperial War Museum: 12.3 (p.110); Jean-Loup Charmet/Science Photo Library: 11.4M; Louvre Ager: 4.7L; Mansell Collection: 10.1B, 12.4S, 13.2G; Mary Evans Picture Library: 8.3F, 10.1 (p.77 top), 11.1 (p.81), 11.1C, 11.2I, 11.3 (p.86), 11.5 (p.90), 12.5 (p.119 top right), 13.5 (2); Michael Holford: 4.3F, 5.3E; Musee Pasteur: 11.3 (p.85), 11.7 (1); National Portrait Gallery: 13.3 (p.129 left); Paul Shuter: 5.3 (p.35); Punch: 13.3P, 13.3S, 13.3T, 13.4Z; Robert Harding: 7.3C, 12.3M; Ronald Sheridan/Ancient Art and Architecture Collection: 4.2D; Royal College of Surgeons: 10.1 (p.77 bottom), 10.1A; Science & Society Picture Library: 11.5 (p.93); Science Photo Library/St Mary's Hospital: 11.5Q, 11.5T; Science Photo Library: 11.7 (5), 12.1G, 12.5 (p.119 top left), 13.3 (p.129 right); The Art Archive/Bardo Museum Tunis/Dagli Orti: 5.6 (3); Timepix/Rex/Mansell Collection: 13.1D; Trinity College, Cambridge: 8.6M; University of Bradford, Calvin Wells Collection:
1.3D; Wellcome Institute Library: 2.5I, 4.2C, 12.1F, 12.2J, 12.4X, 13.2H, 13.2J, 13.5 (1); Werner Forman Archive: 12.4W; West Stowe Country Park: 6D; Zentrale Farbbild Agentur: 9.1B

Cover photo: © Royal College of Surgeons

Written source acknowledgements

The authors and publisher gratefully acknowledge the following publications from which sources in the book have been drawn. In some sources the wording or sentence structure has been simplified:

P. Addison *A New Jerusalem* (Cape, 1985): 13.3U; P. Addison *Now the War is Over* (Cape, 1985): 13.4Y; M. Alexander *Earliest English Poems* (Penguin, 1966): 6A; R.A. Browne *British Latin Selections, AD500-1400* (Blackwell, 1954): 8.7Y; J. Chadwick, W.N. Mann, I.M. Ionie and E.T. Withington *Hippocratic Writings* (Penguin, 1983): 4.3G; M.W Flynn (ed.) *A Report of the Sanitary Conditions of the Labouring Population of Great Britain* (Edinburgh University Press, 1965): 13.2K, 13.2M; GLC *A History of the Black Presence in London* (GLC, 1986): 12.4U; *The Guardian* (27/6/2001): 12.5Y; D. Guthrie *A History of Medicine* (Nelson, 1945): 4.7M, 8.5J; W.O. Hassall *They Saw it Happen 55BC-1485* (Blackwell, 1956): 6B; K. Haeger *The Illustrated History of Surgery* (Harold Starke, 1988): 12.1D; W.H.S. Jones *Pliny's Natural History* (Heinemann, 1923): 5.6 (3); G. Keynes *The Apology and Treatise of Ambroise Pare* (Falcon Educational Books, 1951): 9.3J, 9.3K, 9.3L, 9.3M; H. Lloyd Jones *The Greek World* (Penguin, 1965): 5.6 (1); M.V. Lyons *Medicine in the Medieval World* (Macmillan, 1984): 8.2B, 8.2C, 8.5K; A. McIntosh Gray *Medical Care and Public Health: 1780 to the Present Day* (OUP, 1990): 11.5U, 11.5V; R.H. Major *Classic Descriptions of Disease* (Charles S. Thompson, 1945): 8.7S, 8.7V, 8.7W; V. Nutton 'A Social History of Graeco-Roman Medicine' in *Medicine in Society* (CUP, 1994): 5.2B; E.D. Phillips *Greek Medicine* (Thames and Hudson, 1975): 4.5H, 4.6J; C. Platt *The English Medieval Town* (Granada, 1979): 8.6N; D. Poynter *History at Source: Medicine 300-1929* (Evans Brothers, 1971): 11.5 (4); R. Reid *Microbes and Men* (BBC, 1974): 11.7 (2&3), 12.2I; P. Rhodes *An Outline of the History of Medicine* (Butterworths, 1985): 12.4T; M. Ridley *Disease* (Pheonix, 1997): 11.6Y; SCHP *Medicine Through Time: A Study in Development Book 1* (Holmes McDougal, 1976): 8.7P, 8.7Q, 8.7R; SCHP *Medicine Through Time: A Study in Development Book 3* (Holmes McDougal, 1976): 13.2N; J. Scott *Medicine Through Time* (Holmes McDougal, 1987): 11.1G; R. Shyrock *The Development of Modern Medicine* (London, 1984): 12.6 (2); C. Singer *Galen On Anatomical Procedures* (London, 1956): 5.5K, 9.2C; J.D. de C.M. Saunders and C.D. O'Malley *The Illustrations for the Works of Andreas Vesalius* (World Publishing, 1950): 9.2D; G. Sweetman *A History of Wincanton* (London and Wincanton, 1903): 11.1D; L. Thorndike *Michael Scot* (Nelson, 1965) 8.3E; R. Vallery-Radot *Life of Pasteur* (London, 1911): 11.2H; J.J. Walsh *Medieval Medicine* (London, 1920): 6C; L. M. Zimmerman and I Veith *Great Ideas in the History of Surgery* (London, 1961): 12.2K

CONTENTS

CHAPTER 1

PREHISTORIC MEDICINE

1.1 What was the prehistoric period?

Look at the timeline below. It shows the time covered in this book. Most of the time is prehistoric (before people wrote things down). This makes it difficult for historians to know what happened.

The start of writing

History started as soon as people learned to write. This happened at different times in different parts of the world. Writing started in Egypt long before it started in Britain. So Egypt had a written history when Britain was still prehistoric.

What makes people prehistoric?

- They were nomads (moved from place to place).
- They were hunter gatherers. They hunted animals and picked fruit and berries for food.
- They lived in small groups. There were no towns or roads.
- They had simple tools made from wood, bone or stone.
- They had no writing.

Over many thousands of years two things changed. One was farming. People grew food and stayed in one place. The other was making metal tools.

▲ A cave painting made by prehistoric people in France about 15,000 years ago.

QUESTIONS

1 Read **What makes people prehistoric?**

a Write one sentence about each of the five points.

b Look at the sentences you have written. Which sentence makes it clear that it is difficult for us to know about prehistoric people?

Old Stone Age				New Stone Age		Bronze Age	Iron Age
00 BC	15000 BC	12000 BC	9000 BC	6000 BC	3000 BC	0	AD 2000

Cave paintings in France
Sources A and C

▲ The Stone Age (in most of Europe and the Middle East).

1.2 Prehistoric medicine

We have found the bones of prehistoric peoples. These bones can show that people fell ill or were hurt. We do not know if they used medicine to get better.

Source B

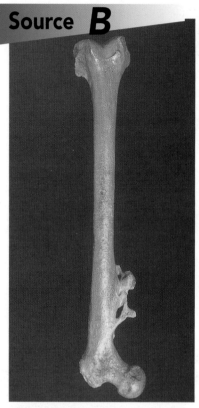

▲ The thigh bone of a prehistoric person. You can clearly see a large growth on the bone.

Source C

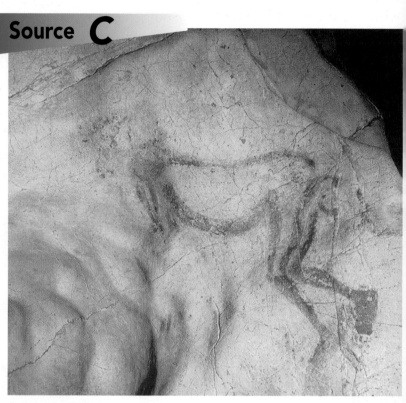

▲ A prehistoric cave painting. Many prehistoric paintings show a man with antlers like this one.

▶ This modern drawing of the cave painting in Source C shows the outline of a man with antlers, possibly wearing a mask, more clearly.

Prehistoric graves of men and women have been found all over the world. The whole skeleton is in the grave. Sometimes there is evidence of trephining. This is when a hole is cut in a person's skull when they are still alive. Often the missing disc of bone is in the grave too. It may have a hole in it as if it had been worn as a lucky charm. Most trephined skulls have rounded edges around the holes. This shows that the person lived for some years after the operation. No children's skulls have been found with holes in them.

Why did prehistoric people cut holes in the heads of living men and women? Historians have puzzled over this for many years. There are four main theories (ideas).

The four main theories about trephining

Theory 1
Dr. Prunieres (1865) suggested the holes were made in the skulls so that they became drinking cups.

Theory 2
Professor Paul Broca (1876) suggested the trephining operation was done on children. Prehistoric people thought that those children who lived on had magical powers.

Theory 3
E. Guiard (1930) suggested trephining was to help illness, such as broken skulls, epilepsy and headaches.

Theory 4
Douglas Guthrie (1945) suggested trephining was to let out evil spirits.

QUESTIONS

1 Look at the sources on pages 6–7. Which source definitely tells us that prehistoric people suffered from illness?

2 Look at the four theories on page 7.

   a Which source contradicts Theory 1?

   b From what you have read on page 7, what might contradict Theory 2?

   c Do you think any of the sources support any of the theories? Explain your answer.

Source D

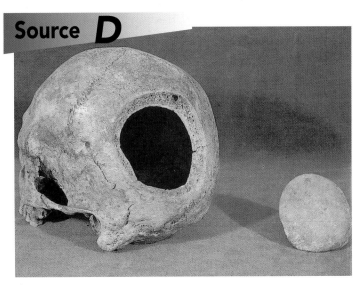

▲ A prehistoric skull. The hole was cut out while the person was alive. We know this because the bone grew afterwards – rounding off the edge.

What do we know about prehistoric medicine?

We know there was some illness. We know that trephining operations were done. But we do not know what prehistoric people thought about illness and medicine. One way to find out is to look at people who have lived in prehistoric ways until recently. This is not the whole answer but it may help.

The Aborigines of Australia

Until about 100 years ago, the Aborigines lived in a way that was in many ways prehistoric. They had no form of writing. They were nomads. They hunted and gathered their food.

Causes of illness – obvious and spirit

The Aborigines felt that some things had an obvious cause. If a person fell and broke her arm it was covered in clay. The clay then set hard so the bone could heal. But some illnesses did not have an obvious cause. The Aborigines believed that such illnesses were caused by spirits.

Aboriginal spirits

The Aborigines thought the world started in the dreamtime. This was when the spirit ancestors lived. These spirits controlled many things. They controlled new life. They controlled where a stream flowed. If a person was sick for no obvious reason, then maybe the sickness was controlled by a spirit.

Spirit causes of illness

The Aborigines had two explanations for sickness caused by spirits. The first was that an evil spirit had entered the sick person's body. The second was that the sick person's spirit had left the body.

If an evil spirit had entered a sick person, the evil spirit had to be driven out. If an enemy had taken the sick person's spirit (possibly using a special bone) the treatment was to find the bone which would have the sick person's spirit stuck to it. Only a spirit treatment would cure a spirit illness.

THE PREHISTORIC PERIOD

Historians divide the prehistoric period into:

Old Stone Age [Palaeolithic] when people were nomadic hunter-gatherers.

New Stone Age [Neolithic] when farming and living in one place became common.

Bronze Age when metal tools were first used.

Iron Age when iron improved the tools and weapons which could be made.

There was an overlap in time between the prehistoric period and those described in the next chapters. For instance, Britain was in the Iron Age during the Greek and early Roman periods.

Source E

▲ An Aboriginal healing amulet. Amulets were tied over painful parts of the body. This one is made of shrub fibres and emu feathers.

Source F

▲ Aborigines using a death bone. This was said to send spirits to kill over long distances.

QUESTIONS

1 Read **Causes of illness – obvious and spirit** on page 8.

  a Write down an injury that had an obvious cause.

  b What was the treatment?

2 Look at Source E. Is an illness caused by a special bone going to need an obvious or a spirit treatment?

3 Would Aborigines use obvious or spirit treatment for the following:

  a A toe cut on a stone

  b A sprained wrist from a fall

  c A heart attack

  d A headache

  e A spear wound?

1.5 Conclusions

We know a little about the way prehistoric people lived. We know this from finding their tools, graves and skeletons. The Aborigines lived in a similar way. Maybe we can learn about prehistoric medicine from looking at the medicine of the Aborigines.

Obvious and spirit reasons for illness

The Aborigines looked at illness in two ways. Maybe prehistoric people also looked at illness in two ways. Maybe they believed that some illnesses were caused by spirits. Maybe trephining was a way to let an evil spirit out of a sick person's head. But we can never really know what people thought, because there are no written records.

1.6 Exercise

Factors affecting medicine

Many factors affect the change and development of medicine over thousands of years. The main factors are listed below with examples.

Factor	Example
Science and technology	The discovery of x-rays in modern times.
War	Plastic surgery for burns in the Second World War.
Religion	Not being allowed to dissect bodies in the Middle Ages.
Government	Roman government was well organized. They built good water systems.
Communications	Writing meant the Egyptians and Chinese could learn more.
Chance	The discovery of penicillin in modern times.

Prehistoric medicine

Copy and complete the chart below. Two boxes have been filled in as examples.

Factor	Question	Answer	Don't know
Science and technology	How much did prehistoric people know about the body and the world around them?		
War	How did war affect medicine?		✓
Religion	How did religion affect medicine?	Prehistoric people probably thought spirits helped to cause and cure disease.	
Government	How well organized were they?		
Communications	Did they write things down?		
Chance	Did unexpected things happen?		

CHAPTER 2

EGYPTIAN MEDICINE

2.1 Ancient Egypt

Life in Ancient Egypt
3000BC–400BC

Life in Egypt was well organized.

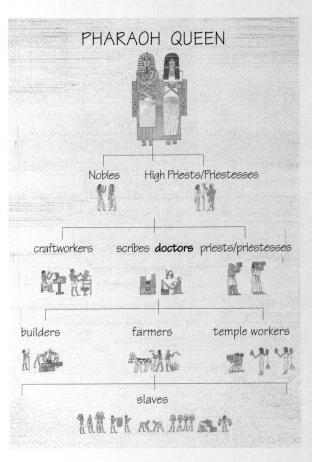

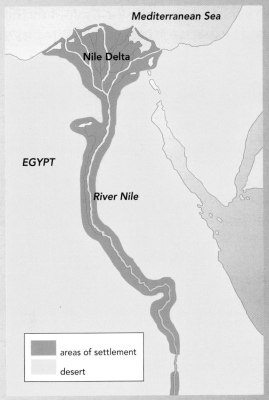

Prehistoric people did not write. Egyptian people did write. Egyptian doctors could write down any cures they discovered. This meant other doctors could learn from them.

Egyptian religion

The Egyptians believed their gods did everything. From making the sun rise to causing and curing illness.

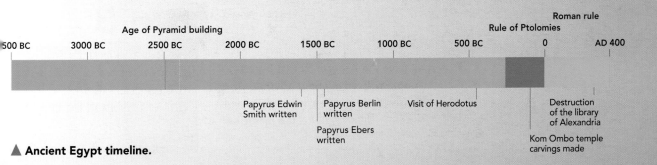

▲ Ancient Egypt timeline.

Causes of disease

Like prehistoric people, the Egyptians thought that many diseases were caused by evil spirits entering the body. They often wore charms to keep evil spirits away.

Medical books

The Egyptians wrote books so we know what they thought about disease. The earliest medical books have been lost. But we do have many later ones. Some of the books are only lists of magical spells for getting rid of evil spirits. Some books, though, tell us about operations, medicines, **hygiene** and diets for sick people.

Medicine and spells

Egyptians made medicines from minerals, animals and plants such as coriander, garlic and figs. The medicines were cooked up and mixed with wine, beer or water (sometimes sweetened with honey). Chest diseases were treated by making the patient breathe in steam. Cuts were covered with **ointment**.

The doctor often gave medicine and said a spell. Together the medicine and spell drove the evil spirits away from the sick person. The doctor did exactly what the medical books said. If the doctor did not do this and the patient died, the doctor might be killed.

The medical books show that, if a cure worked, the doctors kept using it.

Source A

▲ A charm or amulet of the goddess of childbirth. She was called Tawaret. Her face is fierce to drive away evil spirits which hurt the mother or baby.

▶ A spell from the Papyrus Ebers, a medical book, written in about 1500 BC. The doctor chanted the spell while giving the medicine.

Source B

Here is the great remedy. Come! You who drive evil things out. He who drinks this shall be cured.

EGYPTIAN MEDICAL BOOKS

The Ancient Egyptians wrote on papyrus [a kind of paper made from reeds]. A few medical books have survived from that time. They are called after the owner or the museum where they are kept.

The *Papyrus Ebers*, written in about 1500 BC is called after a German, Maurice Ebers.

The *Papyrus Edwin Smith* was bought by Smith in 1862. It was written in about 1600 BC. The book contains spells, medicines and advice on surgery.

2.3 Religion and anatomy

Anatomy and religion

The Egyptians found out how bodies were made (**anatomy**) because they had to cut up bodies as part of their religion. They believed that when a person died, the soul left the body for a while. Then the soul came back and the person began an afterlife. So it was very important to preserve the dead body so that the soul could get back in.

Source C

▲ A painted coffin dated about 600 BC. At the bottom the body is being washed in a natron (salt) solution. In the middle the body is covered with natron crystals during the 40 day drying-out stage. At the top, on the left, the embalmed body (called a mummy) is in the tomb above four jars. The jars hold the liver, lungs, stomach and intestines. On the right the god, Anubis, is with the mummy.

Source D

Forty-six vessels go from the heart to every limb. Wherever a doctor places his hands he hears the heart.

▲ From the *Papyrus Ebers*, about 1500 BC.

Embalming but not dissecting

The Egyptians preserved dead bodies by soaking them in different liquids, covering them in oils and wrapping them in bandages. This was called **embalming**.

The Egyptians understood a great deal about bodies because they cut them open to embalm them. They knew where **organs** like the heart and lungs were.

But they did not do any more cutting up. This was because they believed that the body must be kept for a life after death.

2.4 A natural theory of the causes of disease

A new, natural theory

The River Nile was vital to life in Egypt. Without the river and its seasonal flooding, no crops could be grown.

The Egyptians looked at the River Nile with all its channels and ditches. Perhaps the human body was like this. Perhaps it was full of channels and ditches carrying blood, food and water around it. If these channels got blocked a person would become ill. Doctors who believed in this idea used a number of treatments.

To clear the blocks

- Some doctors thought that making the patient sick would clear the blockage.
- Purges (**laxatives**) were use to clear the lower end of the body.
- Bleeding was also used. The doctor cut open a vein to clear the blood channels.

Natural and spiritual causes of disease side by side

Not all doctors liked the idea of channels in the body. Some preferred the idea of spirits causing disease.

The *Papyrus Ebers*, a medical book, gives spells for getting rid of illness.

It also lists herbs to use to make sick people better. Often the herbs helped to unblock the channels.

▲ Treatment from the *Papyrus Ebers*, about 1500 BC.

2.5 Surgery

Surgery

Doctors passed their jobs on from father to son (or sometimes daughter). Some doctors may have carried out small surgical operations but probably not major ones.

Minor operations

The *Papyrus Edwin Smith* described some of these simple operations. The Egyptians set **dislocated** arms and legs. They set broken bones. They cut away small **cysts** and tumours. They used the leaves and bark of the willow tree to bind up wounds. We now know that willow is a kind of **antiseptic**. It helped to stop wounds going bad. This meant that many people probably recovered from these small operations.

Source G

If a man has a dislocation of the jaw and cannot close it, put your thumbs on the ends of the two rami of the lower jawbone, inside the mouth. Put your fingers under his chin and make them fall back into the correct position.

▲ From the *Papyrus Edwin Smith*, about 1600 BC.

Source H

When you come across a swelling that moves under your moving finger and the patient is clammy, then you say, 'I will treat it with fire since cautery heals it.'

When a swelling is like a hard stone under your fingers, then you say, 'I will treat the disease with a knife.'

▲ From the *Papyrus Ebers*, about 1500 BC.

Source I

◀ A carving showing Egyptian surgical instruments. These include saws, forceps, scalpels and scissors. They were usually made from bronze, although some surgical knives were made of flint.

Keeping clean

The Egyptians washed every day. The priests washed even more often. Maybe keeping clean had more to do with religion than with health. But, whatever the reason, keeping clean helped the Egyptians to keep healthy.

Water

The Egyptians used the water from the River Nile to water their crops. They had lots of ditches carrying the river water to the fields. But they did not have water flushed toilets. Toilets were a stone seat over a jar. Rich people had baths but these just drained into a jar too. The jars could be taken to the fields by slaves. This manured and watered the fields.

▲ An artist's reconstruction of an Egyptian toilet seat made of limestone.

Source J

The Egyptians drink from cups of bronze which they clean daily. They keep their clothes clean.

Their priests shave their whole bodies and wash three times a day.

▲ From *The Histories* by the Greek historian Herodotus, about 450 BC.

QUESTIONS

1 Copy the following statements about Egyptian medicine.

   a Many Egyptians thought that the best way to keep healthy was to wear a charm or amulet.

   b Some Egyptian doctors used spells and medicine together.

   c Egyptian doctors knew some anatomy. They knew about the heart, lungs and brain. This was because they embalmed dead bodies.

   d Egyptian doctors used treatments based on giving herbs such as senna and fruit of sycamore.

   e Egyptian doctors treated dislocations.

   f Egyptian doctors treated tumours.

   g Egyptians used toilets and kept clean.

2 For each statement write down the source that supports it. Use all the sources in this chapter.

3 Egyptians thought that wearing charms would keep them healthy. Was this a new idea? Explain your answer.

2.7 Exercise

Study the sources below and then answer the questions.

Source 1

EXAMINATION
If you examine a man whose nose is disfigured – part being squashed in, while the other part is swollen and both his nostrils are bleeding.

DIAGNOSIS
Then you should say, 'You have a broken nose and this is something I can treat.'

TREATMENT
You should clean his nose and insert two plugs soaked in grease in his nostrils. You should make him rest until his swelling has gone down, and bandage his nose with stiff rolls of linen.

▲ From the *Papyrus Edwin Smith*, written in about 1600 BC.

Source 2

These words are to be spoken over the sick person: 'Oh spirit, male or female, who lurks hidden in my flesh and my limbs, get out of my flesh! Get out of my limbs!'

▲ From the *Papyrus Berlin*, written in about 1450 BC.

Source 3

▶ Imhotep, Vizier to the Pharaoh Zoser, about 2630 BC. Imhotep may have been Zoser's doctor as well. He is probably the earliest doctor whose name we know. He was later worshipped by the Egyptians as a god of healing.

Read Sources 1 and 2.

1 a What is the diagnosis in Source 1?

  b What do you think is wrong with the patient in Source 2?

  c Why do you think the Ancient Egyptians followed two different ideas about treating sick people?

2 Did the Ancient Egyptians understand about keeping clean to avoid illness? Explain your answer.

Egyptian medicine

Copy and complete the chart below. Two boxes have been filled in as examples.

Factor	Question	Answer	Don't know
Science and Technology	How much did they know about the body and the world around?	They knew some anatomy – heart, lungs etc. They had a new theory about channels in the body.	
War	Did war affect medicine?		
Religion	How did religion affect medicine?		
Government	How well organized were they?		
Communications	Did they write things down?		
Chance	Did unexpected things happen?		✓

CHAPTER 3

MINOAN CRETE

3.1 Who were the Minoans?

The Minoans lived on the island of Crete. Their civilization was at its best about 3000 years ago.

Archaeologists have found many Minoan buildings.

We also know about the Minoans from Greek writers.

Minoan hygiene

Archaeologists have found several Minoan palaces. The most famous is at Knossos.

They have found water tanks to collect rain water. They have also found lavatories and drains, which took away the sewage.

▼One of the stone drains at the Minoan palace of Knossos. It carried dirty water away.

Source A

SIR ARTHUR EVANS

The Minoan palace of Knossos was excavated by Sir Arthur Evans.

Evans bought land in Crete. In 1900, he began digging and found the large palace at Knossos.

He found room after room. He worked out what he thought the rooms were used for.

Archaeologists today do not agree with all of his ideas.

Aqueducts?

Some of the pipes at Knossos might have brought water from far away. It is possible that the Minoans built **aqueducts** (bridges which carry water) to cross valleys. No one knows for certain.

3.2 The legacy of the Minoans

Source **B**

▲ The Queen's bathroom at Knossos.

The Minoan palaces destroyed

The palaces were destroyed by fire over 3000 years ago.

No one knows what destroyed them. Some historians think a volcano erupted nearby and set off earthquakes. Others think that the Greeks attacked and burnt the palaces.

What happened to the Minoans?

No one knows. But all the skill of the Minoans in building water systems was lost. No one built water systems and aqueducts until Roman times. This loss of knowledge is called regression. Knowledge lost had to be rediscovered later.

CHANCE

Many changes happen by chance. This means that they happen by accident, not because someone has set out to make them happen.

If the Minoan civilization had not been destroyed then their ideas about keeping clean could have been passed on.

The progress of medicine was held up by the collapse of the Minoan civilization. No one intended this to happen.

QUESTIONS

1 Read **Minoan hygiene**. What two things did the Minoans build that show they knew about keeping clean?

2 What stopped the Minoans from passing on their ideas?

CHAPTER 4

ANCIENT GREECE

4.1 Greece 1000 – 300 BC

Ancient Greece was not one country. The Greek people lived on the land and islands around the eastern Mediterranean (see map). They built many cities. Each city ruled itself. Sometimes they fought each other.

Greek language and gods

Greek people spoke the same language, wherever they lived. They believed in the same gods. The gods were a way of explaining how the world worked.

Why there was winter

Demeter was the goddess of agriculture. Her daughter had to spend half the year in the underworld. This made Demeter angry. She did not allow plants to grow while her daughter was in the underworld. So this made the winter time.

Why there were volcanoes

The god of fire was a blacksmith. His name was Hephaestos. He made the smoke and fire of volcanoes. This was when he was working at his forge.

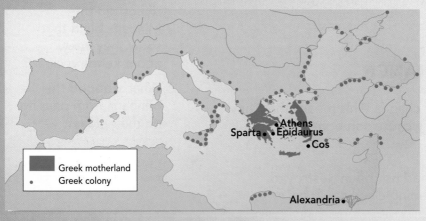

◀ **The Greek world, in about 450 BC. Alexandria is in Egypt at the mouth of the River Nile.**

Greek motherland
Greek colony

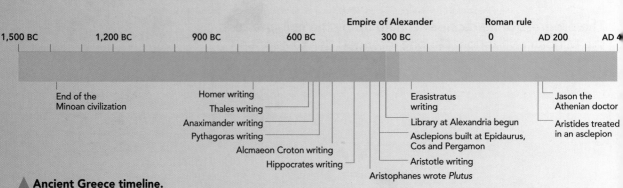

▲ **Ancient Greece timeline.**

Greek civilization 600 – 300 BC

Greek people were rich and powerful at this time. They made money from trade and farming. Some people were very rich. They did not have to work. So they had plenty of time to enjoy themselves. They also had plenty of time to think.

Pythagoras and other great thinkers

Pythagoras had completely new ideas in mathematics. He thought up a new theorem. Thales of Miletus studied **astronomy** and put forward the idea that water was the basis of life. Anaximander used this idea about water to work out his own ideas. He said all things were made from four elements – water, fire, earth and air.

▲ A hero from the siege of Troy treats his wounded friend. This painting is from a decorated cup.

CHANGE AND DEVELOPMENT

A **change** is a completely new idea.

A **development** is when something is based on what went before it – it has *developed* from a previous idea.

Greek medicine

We first know about Greek medicine from the poems of Homer. He wrote about war and treating wounded soldiers. Later, more Greek people wrote about medicine. One of the most famous was Hippocrates.

Rational medicine and supernatural medicine

Hippocrates was interested in **rational** medicine. He wanted to work out why things happened. He wrote a number of books about medicine in about 430 BC.

The other sort of medicine was **supernatural** medicine. This was to do with spirits and the god Asclepios. This kind of medicine was very popular around and after 400 BC.

QUESTIONS

1 Look at the map on page 20. Could the Greeks have known about Egyptian medicine?

2 Read **CHANGE AND DEVELOPMENT** and **Pythagoras and other great thinkers**.

a Were the ideas of Pythagoras a change or a development?

b Were the ideas of Anaximander a change or a development?

Supernatural medicine

Asclepios was the Greek god of healing. The Greeks built temples to worship him. Sick people would go to one of the temples. They spent at least one night there. The sick person would probably have:

- Given a gift to the god Asclepios.
- Washed in the sea.
- Slept in a part of the temple called the *abaton*.

The sick person expected to be visited by Asclepios. Some people had dreams. The priests probably treated people while they were asleep. The snake was Asclepios' sacred animal. Sometimes the priests used snakes as part of the treatment.

How we know

Sick people were supposed to wake up cured. Sometimes they did. Sometimes they did not. Aristides, who came from Athens, visited many temples of Asclepios. He wrote about some treatment he had in AD 150. Aristophanes also wrote about treatment in a play called *Plutus* in about 370 BC.

Source B

First we had to bathe Plutus in the sea.

Then we entered the temple and gave our offerings. There were many sick people. Soon the temple priest put out the light and told us to sleep. The god sat down by Plutus. He wiped his head and eyelids.

Next Panacea [the god's daughter] covered his face with a scarlet cloth. The god whistled and two snakes came.

They licked Plutus' eyelids and he could see again. But the god and his helpers had gone.

▲ From *Plutus*, a play written by Aristophanes. Plutus was cured of blindness.

Source C

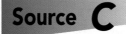

▶ A model of the temple to Asclepios at Epidaurus.

Continuity

For hundreds of years sick people visited religious places. They wanted to be cured. Sick people visited the temples of Asclepios from about 300 BC to about AD 400. In the Middle Ages, in Britain and Europe, sick people visited great churches. Until a few years ago sick people in parts of Greece, Italy and Sicily spent the night in a church. They all hoped to be cured.

We are looking at change in the history of medicine. But it is important to know that there was **continuity** too.

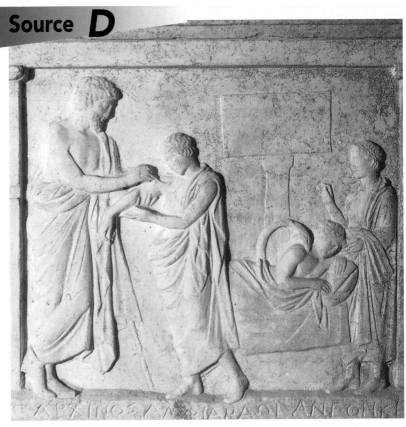

▲ A carving showing Asclepios treating a boy called Archinos. This was made about 350 BC.

Source E

- Ambrosia became blind in one eye. She had laughed at cures before. But she dreamed Asclepios said he would cure her if she gave a silver pig. He seemed to cut into her eyeball and pour in medicine. When she woke she was cured.

- Euhippus had a spear point in his jaw for six years. As he was sleeping in the temple Asclepios pulled it out.

- While a man slept in the temple a snake licked his diseased toe. He woke cured.

▲ Writings in stone, called *Iamata*, at a temple to Asclepios. Many such writings recording cures have been found.

QUESTIONS

1 Look at Sources B–E. They are all about Asclepios. Answer the following questions.

  a When was each source made or written?

  b How reliable is each source?

  c How useful is each source to an historian?

Hippocrates and balance

Hippocrates learnt from two earlier thinkers called Pythagoras and Alcmaeon of Croton. They taught that a body was healthy when all the parts were in balance, and neither too hot nor too cold.

The Hippocratic Corpus (books)

Hippocrates left a collection of medical books called the *Hippocratic Corpus*. He probably did not write all of them himself. The books are important because they tell us about Greek medicine.

What Hippocrates did not want

Hippocrates did not want doctors to think that illness was caused or cured by magic. He also did not want doctors to have just one theory about illness which fitted every patient.

What Hippocrates did want

Hippocrates wanted doctors to watch their sick patients carefully and to treat them according to what was going on. This is called **clinical observation**. This was not a new idea. The Egyptians had also believed in watching the patient for **symptoms**. For instance, doctors should watch a patient with a cold. Then next time they would know what was likely to happen and what to do about it.

CLINICAL OBSERVATION

A doctor watches all the changes in a person during an illness.

Diagnosis
What's wrong? (Sneezing)

Prognosis
What is going to happen? (After sneezing comes shivering)

Observation
Keep watching. (After shivering comes coughing)

Treatment
The doctor should give medicine only when he is sure of what is wrong with the sick person.

► The tombstone of Jason, a doctor from Athens, who died in the 2nd century AD. Jason is shown examining a patient.

Source F

Hippocrates also said sick people should be kept clean and quiet. A doctor should only give medicine if he was sure he knew what was wrong with the patient.

Surgery

The Greeks did not allow anyone to cut up dead bodies. So surgeons did not know where things were inside the body. This was dangerous for the patient! Most surgery was simple, such as setting breaks and resetting dislocated bones.

Source G

A person with quinsey shivers, has a headache, swelling under the jaw and dry mouth.

He cannot spit or breathe lying down. He must be bled and made to breathe in a mixture of vinegar and soda heated in oil and water. Hot sponges must be put on his neck.

He must gargle herbs and have his throat cleaned out.

▲ From a Hippocratic book called *On Diseases*.

4.4 The four humours

Aristotle (384–322 BC)

Many Hippocratic books said that bodies needed to be in balance to be well. Some of the books talked about balancing four humours. However, Aristotle took the ideas much further.

He said that the body was made up of four liquids or humours. Each humour was connected to a season (see diagram).

The body could get out of balance. For instance, lots of people got colds in winter. They had too much **phlegm**.

The right treatment by the doctor was to give medicines to clear the phlegm.

This would bring the four humours back into balance in the body.

A person with a hot fever probably had too much blood in the body. In this case the doctor would cut a vein and take some blood out of the body. This was called 'bleeding' the patient.

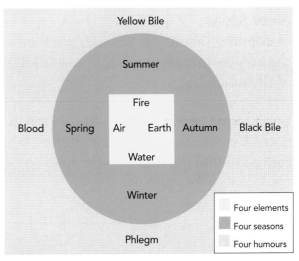

▲ The four humours.

Alexander the Great

Alexander the Great conquered a lot of land. He built a great, new city in Egypt in 332 BC. He called it Alexandria. The city became famous for its library. It also became a great place for the study of medicine. Many doctors were trained at Alexandria.

The study of medicine – dissection

The Greeks did not allow **dissection** of dead bodies. But thinkers like Aristotle said that the soul of a dead person left the body. It did not matter if you cut up the dead body.

Dissection in Alexandria

Not everyone liked Aristotle's ideas. However, dissection was allowed in Alexandria. Doctors learned a lot about bodies. For a time even live bodies were cut up. These were criminals who were going to be executed. In this way the doctors saw how the blood moved in the veins.

Was surgery safer?

Doctors in Alexandria knew a lot more about bodies. However, having an operation was still very dangerous. There were no **anaesthetics** and no one knew much about keeping wounds clean.

New ideas

Herophilus (about 335–280 BC) put forward the idea that the nerves were channels that carried the life force or pneuma.

Erasistratus (about 250 BC) studied the human body and noted the difference between arteries, veins and nerves. He found that the nerves were solid so he said that they could not carry pneuma.

Source H

Chest trouble starts with sweating, a salty, bitter mouth, pains in the ribs and shoulder blades, shaking hands and dry cough. Treat with pounded radishes, cardamons, mustard, purslane and rocket in warm water. This will cause a healing vomit.

▲ From a book by Diocles, a Greek doctor who lived in Alexandria in the 4th century BC.

QUESTIONS

1 Look at page 24. Read **Hippocrates and balance**.

a Who did Hippocrates learn from?

b Was Hippocratic medicine a change or a development?

2 Look at page 25.

Below are the four humours. Copy them out as a list. Write the correct season next to each one.

● Blood
● Yellow Bile
● Black Bile
● Phlegm

Source I

▲ A vase painting, from 333 BC. It shows young men racing. The Greeks thought that exercise kept people healthy.

Source J

After waking, a man should wait a little. Then get up. He should rub his body with oil. Then wash in pure water.

He should rub his teeth with his finger using peppermint powder. He should oil his nose, ears and hair every day. And wash his hair less often.

After this he should go to work. If he does not need to work, he should go for a walk. This clears out the body. He is then ready to eat.

▲ From a book by Diocles, a Greek doctor.

▶ A vase painting, from about 450 BC showing women washing.

Keeping healthy

The Greeks said that eating and drinking affected your health. They also thought that exercise, work and sleep affected your health.

Hippocratic books

Some of the books set out what a person should or should not eat. How much a person drank was important. They said how much exercise a person should take. They said keeping clean was important. So was getting enough sleep.

Many doctors told their patients how to live a healthy life. This was better than waiting until they were ill and then taking medicine.

Source K

The spread of Greek medicine

Greek doctors travelled all around the lands by the Mediterranean Sea. Other doctors learnt from the Greeks. Over the years Greek ideas about medicine spread far and wide.

A code of conduct – the Hippocratic Oath

Hippocrates said it was very important that a doctor behaved well. He should take an **oath** to do his best.

The idea that doctors should behave well is still followed today.

Clinical observation

The Greeks said that clinical observation was very important. Doctors should always see a patient before giving medicine. Records should be kept of a patient's illnesses.

All these things are still done today.

Source **L**

▲ A Greek painted vase, from about 400 BC. The doctor is sitting in the centre of the painting. To his right is a man he is about to bleed. There is a large bowl on the floor to catch the blood.

Source **M**

I swear by Apollo, by Asclepios, and by all the gods and goddesses that I will carry out this oath.

I will use treatment to help the sick according to my ability and judgment but never with a view to injury or wrong-doing.

▲ A small part of the Hippocratic Oath quoted in D. Guthrie, *A History of Medicine*, 1945.

QUESTIONS

1 a Below are some Greek ideas about medicine. Write one sentence explaining each one.

- The cult of Asclepios (page 22)
- Clinical observation (page 28)
- The four humours (page 25)
- Keeping healthy (page 27)
- The Hippocratic Oath (page 28)

b Which of the ideas above are similar to modern medicine? Which ones are different?

4.8 Exercise

Study the following sources.

Source 1

Hermodicius was paralysed in his body. When he slept in the temple the god healed him and ordered him to bring to the temple as large a stone as he could.

▲ **An inscription found at a temple to Asclepios.**

Source 2

In an Asclepion the patient believed he would get better. Other treatments consisted of diet, drugs, exercise, baths and massage. The patient could relax by visiting the nearby theatre.

▲ **A description of how Asceplions worked.**

Read Source 1.

1 a What was the matter with Hermodicius?

b What do we learn about Greek medicine from this source?

Read Source 2.

2 a Write a list of all the things that helped to make a patient better according to this source.

b Does Source 2 suggest that Aesclepions were examples of supernatural or rational medicine? Explain your answer.

3 Was Hippocrates interested in rational or supernatural medicine?

4 What did Hippocrates do to help the development of medicine?

Greek medicine

Copy and complete the chart below. Two boxes have been filled in as examples.

Factor	Question	Answer	Don't know
Science and Technology	How much did they know about the body and the world around?	New ideas about the world made doctors look at the body in a new way.	
War	How did war affect medicine?		
Religion	How did religion affect medicine?		
Government	How well organized were they?		
Communications	Did they write things down?		
Chance	Did unexpected things happen?	Yes – for example the *Hippocratic Corpus*.	

CHAPTER 5

ROMAN MEDICINE

5.1 Roman civilization

How Rome ruled

Rome conquered the rest of Italy. The Romans then conquered more and more land, and built up a huge **empire** (see map below). The Romans were well organized. They built good roads and used them to send officials and armies to govern their empire.

Usually everyone did what the government in Rome said because they were backed up by a large army. So it was important to keep the soldiers in this army healthy. The Romans thought a lot about how to prevent disease.

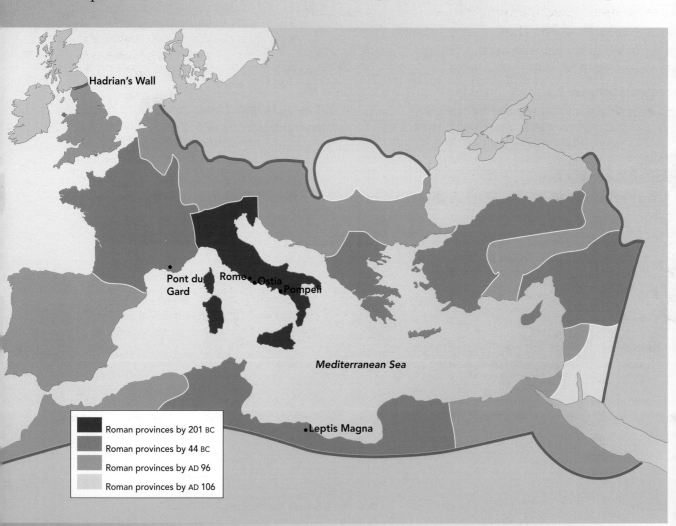

Hadrian's Wall

Pont du Gard

Rome · Ostia

Pompeii

Mediterranean Sea

· Leptis Magna

Roman provinces by 201 BC

Roman provinces by 44 BC

Roman provinces by AD 96

Roman provinces by AD 106

▲ The Roman Empire.

5.2 Medicine in early Rome

Respect for doctors?

At first there were not many doctors in Rome. People treated their families with herbs, common sense (rest if you are ill) and some superstitious ideas. When Rome conquered Greece (about 250 BC) they took some Greeks back to Rome with them as slaves. Some of these were doctors. They only had a low status, but, gradually, more and more Romans went to see Greek doctors. They also used some Greek ideas on spiritual cures. They built a temple to Asclepios. This temple in Rome treated poor people and slaves.

Keeping people healthy

The Romans ruled many countries. They needed a big army to keep order. They needed the soldiers to be healthy. They set up hospitals for soldiers all over the Roman Empire. They also set up hospitals for the civil servants who collected taxes and kept the law. They paid state doctors to care for the poor.

QUESTIONS

1 Read **How Rome ruled** on page 30.

 a How did the Roman government send orders to the cities it ruled?

 b Why did everyone do what the government in Rome said?

2 Look at Source B.

 a From what race of people did most doctors come?

 b Look at the caption to Source B. Why do we have to be careful about believing this source?

Source B

Social and ethnic status of Roman doctors from the 1st to the 3rd century AD

	Total	Greek
Citizens	186	118
Freedmen (ex slaves)	170	158
Slaves	55	54
Foreign, non-citizens	31	23
Total	442	353

◀ This table lists all the doctors for whom tombstones have been found. Obviously this is not all the doctors for those 300 years.

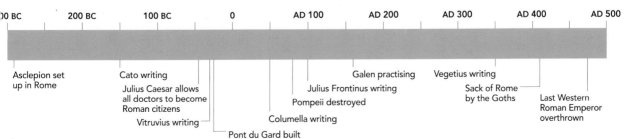

Ancient Rome timeline.

- 00 BC
- 200 BC
- 100 BC
- 0
- AD 100
- AD 200
- AD 300
- AD 400
- AD 500

Asclepion set up in Rome

Cato writing

Julius Caesar allows all doctors to become Roman citizens

Vitruvius writing

Pont du Gard built

Columella writing

Pompeii destroyed

Julius Frontinus writing

Galen practising

Vegetius writing

Sack of Rome by the Goths

Last Western Roman Emperor overthrown

▲ Ancient Rome timeline.

Greek doctors become Roman citizens

Greek doctors still had low status, even though they were used more and more. Then, in 46 BC, Julius Caesar made a law that Greek doctors could become Roman citizens. Some Greek doctors became rich and famous.

5.3 Public health

How to keep healthy

The Romans noticed that people who lived near the marshes around Rome often died from a fever. We now call this fever malaria. They built a temple to the goddess of fever and drained the marshes. Far fewer people got malaria.

What does this say about Roman public health?

1 The Romans did not know that mosquitoes who live in marshes spread malaria by biting human beings. However, the Romans saw that marshes were unhealthy so they got rid of them.

2 Draining the marshes was not easy or cheap. But the Romans were very clever, rich and well organized. They could take on large engineering work like draining marshes or building bridges.

Roman ideas about bad health

The Romans believed you could be made ill by:

- bad smells
- bad water
- marshes
- being near sewage
- not keeping clean.

The Romans did not know why these things caused bad health. But when they built a house or an army camp, they made sure to keep away from bad and dirty places. They also tried to clean up the towns and cities.

Source C

The new Anio aqueduct is taken from the river which is muddy because of the ploughed fields on either side. Because of this water is filtered at the start of the aqueduct.

▲ Julius Frontinus, the Curator of Rome's water supply, writing in about AD 100.

Source D

There should be no marshes near buildings. Marshes give off poisonous vapours during the summer. At this time they give birth to animals with mischief-making stings.

▲ Written by Columella, a Roman writer, who lived in the 1st century AD. He was a soldier who became a farmer and writer of books on country life.

Source **E**

▲ The Pont du Gard aqueduct, which carried water from Uzes to the Roman town at Nîmes in southern France.

Source **F**

We must take care in choosing springs [from which to pipe water].

If a spring runs free and open, look carefully at the people who live nearby before beginning to pipe the water. If they are strong and well then the water is good.

▲ Vitruvius, a Roman writer and architect who lived in the 1st century BC.

Source **G**

▲ A modern artist's reconstruction of toilets on Hadrian's Wall. Water ran through a channel under the seats to wash away the sewage.

Source **H**

▲ The smaller inner arch is the original outlet of Rome's main sewer into the River Tiber. From the water to the top of the arch is over 2m in height.

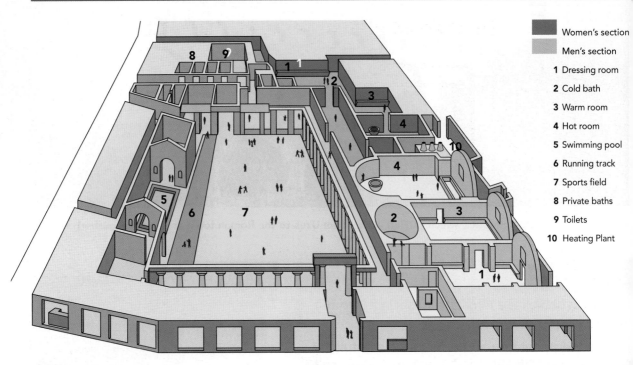

Women's section
Men's section

1 Dressing room
2 Cold bath
3 Warm room
4 Hot room
5 Swimming pool
6 Running track
7 Sports field
8 Private baths
9 Toilets
10 Heating Plant

▲ Stabian Baths at Pompeii.

Aqueducts

The Romans built aqueducts to bring water to towns. There were fourteen aqueducts bringing water to Rome from the hills around the city. There were no pumps so all the aqueducts ran gently down the hill to the city. The water was used for baths, cooking and other things.

Source *I*

◄ The warm room of the men's section of the Stabian Baths.

Emperor 17.1%

Private houses and industry 38.6%

Military barracks 2.9%

Official buildings 24.1%

Public buildings, baths and theatres 3.9%

Public cisterns and fountains 13.4%

▲ The way Rome's water supply was used in AD 100.

THE FORUM PUBLIC TOILETS, POMPEII

▲ The area marked **a** on the plan.

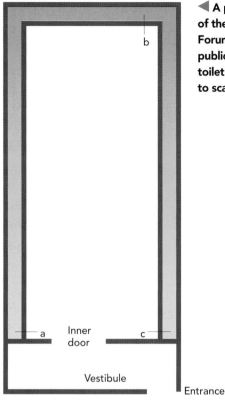

◀ A plan of the Forum public toilet (not to scale).

b

Inner door

a

c

Vestibule

Entrance

▲ The area marked **b** on the plan.

▲ Looking inside from the vestibule.

▲ The view from the inner door.

▲ The area marked **c** on the plan.

Compare these toilets with the artist's impression of the toilets on Hadrian's Wall (Source G on page 33).

What do **a**, **b** and **c** on this plan show?

How are the two toilets the same?

How are they different?

▲ The entrance to the men's toilet from the Forum.

Roman toilets

Roman towns had lots of public toilets. Rome had 150! People did not see going to the toilet as a private thing. There were no separate cubicles. People sat and chatted.

Roman baths

Bathing was even more sociable. A bath house had hot, warm and cold baths. It also had a steam room. Bathers could use the gym or have a massage. Men and women had separate bath houses. If there was only one bath house they used it on different days.

The poor

The poor in the cities were not as lucky as the rich. They did not have running water piped to their homes. They also did not have toilets with pipes which drained into the sewers. They used chamber pots instead, which they sometimes emptied in the street. So not all Roman streets were clean and healthy.

QUESTIONS

1 Look at page 32. What five things did the Romans believe caused bad health?

2 a Copy this statement: The Romans did not like to build a town near a marsh.

  b Which source(s) support this statement?

3 a Copy this statement: The Romans believed that clean water was important for health.

  b Which source(s) support this statement?

4 a Copy this statement: The Romans believed it was important to get rid of sewage.

  b Which source(s) support this statement?

5.4 The army

It was especially important to keep Roman soldiers healthy. Soldiers with good medical skills looked after other soldiers on the battlefield. There were army hospitals. Army camps were built in healthy places. They were kept clean. Permanent bases, such as forts, often had bath houses, toilets and sewage disposal.

Source J

Soldiers must not remain too long near unhealthy marshes.

A soldier who must face the cold without proper clothing is not in a state to have good health or to march.

He must not drink swamp water.

The generals believe daily exercise is better for soldiers than doctors.

▶ Vegetius, a Roman writer in the 4th century AD.

Galen's life

AD 129   Born in Pergamum.
Grew up and trained as a doctor at the temple of Asclepios. Went to Alexandria to study.

AD 157   Returned to Pergamum. Became doctor to the gladiators. He was able to see inside the body because of the wounds suffered by the gladiators.

AD 161   Went to Rome and became famous. He told everyone how good he was.

AD 169   Was given the job of doctor to the Emperor's son. From then on he wrote many books.

Galen as a doctor

Galen was a good doctor. Like Hippocrates, Galen said that a doctor must watch his patient carefully (clinical observation). He must write down all the symptoms of an illness.

The four humours and the idea of opposites

Galen used the theory of the four humours and the need to keep the patient in balance. He based a lot of his treatments on opposites. So, if a woman came to him with the symptoms of a cold, he would give a treatment which included pepper or ginger or other warming herbs.

Galen and human anatomy

When Galen was in Alexandria he had studied human skeletons. But he had not been able to dissect human bodies. By this time dissection was forbidden for religious reasons.

Source K

Part of Galen's experiment on a pig to show the importance of the spinal cord.

The animal which you vivisect should not be old – so that it will be easy for you to cut through the vertebrae.

If you cut by the thoracic vertebrae then the first thing that happens is that you see the animal's breathing and voice have been damaged.

If you cut through between the fifth vertebra of the head, then both arms are paralysed.

▲ From *On Anatomical Procedures*, written by Galen in the late 2nd century AD.

However, back in Pergamum and Rome, Galen and other doctors could not even study human skeletons.

How could doctors learn about the human body?

Galen suggested that they should keep a look out for human bones – in cemeteries or after a hanging when a body had been left out to rot.

Galen and animals

Galen learnt as much as he could from dissecting animals. He said barbary apes were most like humans. He also dissected pigs. Using animals gave him problems with things like the brain. He said the brain had a network of blood vessels on the underside. He based a lot of his ideas on this. However, this network is only found in some animals. It is not found in humans.

Why was Galen so important?

Galen was very important for a number of reasons.

1 He wrote over 100 medical books. Most of the books survived. Just having his ideas known about made him important.

2 He developed the ideas of Hippocrates and other great doctors.

3 From these ideas, he developed a complete theory of medicine. He wrote about how the human body works and what happens when it goes wrong. This was very helpful to doctors for hundreds of years.

4 He lived at a time when the Romans still believed in many gods. But he often wrote about 'the creator' or the great designer of the human body. This meant that Christians and Muslims, who only believed in one god, accepted his ideas. In fact, Galen's ideas dominated medicine in Europe for the next 1300 years.

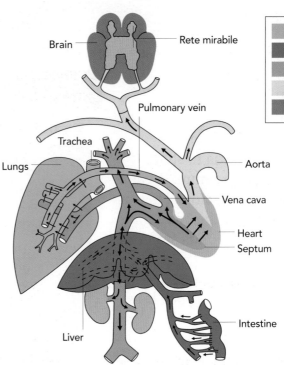

Brain — Rete mirabile
Pulmonary vein
Trachea
Lungs
Aorta
Vena cava
Heart
Septum
Intestine
Liver

	pneuma
	chyle
	blood with natural spirit
	blood with vital spirit
	blood with animal spirit

Pneuma (life-giving spirit) was breathed in, went from the lungs to the heart and mixed with the blood.

Chyle (the goodness from food) went from the intestines to the liver where it was made into blood with Natural Spirit.

Blood with Natural Spirit went throughout the body nourishing and enabling growth. From the heart some went to the lungs, and some passed through the septum where it mixed with the pneuma to form blood with Vital Spirit.

Blood with Vital Spirit went into the arteries giving power to the body. When this blood reached the brain it was changed into blood with Animal Spirit.

Blood with Animal Spirit went through the nerves (which Galen believed were hollow) to give the body sensation and motion.

▲ **Galen's physiological system.**

QUESTIONS

1 Read **Galen's life** on page 37.

a How old was Galen when he became doctor to the gladiators?

b How would treating gladiators give Galen more experience in anatomy than treating ordinary men and women?

2 Read **Why was Galen so important?**

a How do we know about Galen?

b Whose ideas did Galen develop?

c Why did Galen appeal to Christians and Muslims as well as Romans?

3 Read **Galen and human anatomy** on page 37.

a What was forbidden in Alexandria that made Galen's study of anatomy difficult?

b What else was forbidden in Pergamum that made Galen's study of anatomy difficult?

5.6 Exercise

Study the following sources.

Source 1

The school of medicine founded by Hippocrates spread all over Greece. His methods of observing and recording a patient's symptoms were scientific. The aim was to say what would happen in an illness.

▲ Hugh Lloyd Jones, *The Greek World*, 1965.

Source 3

When Marcus Agrippa was in charge of the sewers he travelled under Rome in a boat. There are seven tunnels in the city which run into one great sewer. The rain water sweeps away all the city's sewage.

▲ Adapted from Pliny's *Natural History*, written in Rome in about AD 50.

Source 2

There is no doubt that all these Greek doctors hunt for popularity by using new ideas. They do not hesitate to buy this popularity with our lives.

▲ Pliny criticising Greek doctors working in Rome.

Read Source 1.
1 a What was scientific about Hippocrates' methods ?

   b What was his aim?

Read Source 2.
2 What does Pliny say about the Greek doctors?

3 Why do you think Pliny criticised the Greek doctors?

Read Source 3.
4 Does this source have anything to do with health and medicine? Explain your answer.

Roman medicine

Copy and complete the chart below. Two boxes have been filled in as examples.

Factor	Question	Answer	Don't know
Science and Technology	How much did they know about the body and the world around them?		
War	How did war affect medicine?		
Religion	How did religion affect treatment?		
Government	How well organized were they?	1 They had a strong government. 2 They had a large army. 3 They had good water systems.	
Communications	How good were communications?		
Chance	Did unexpected things happen?		✓

Source 1

The cult of Asclepios spread throughout Greece. Soon there were more than 200 Asclepions. The cult was carried to Rome in 293 BC by Greek priests. The Greek ships sailed up the river to Rome. A sacred serpent sprang from the ship and swam ashore. A temple to Asclepios was built on this spot.

▲ From a book written on the history of medicine in 1954.

Source 2

▲ A Roman coin, dated 291 BC, depicting the arrival of the serpent on an island in the River Tiber.

Source 3

▲ A Roman carving of the God Asclepios dating from about AD 200.

Read Source 1.
1 Do you think the Romans believed that Asclepions worked? Explain your answer.

Look at Source 2.
2 Does this source prove that what is said in Source 1 must have happened? Explain your answer.

3 a How many years are there between the cult of Asclepios arriving in Rome and the carving in Source 3?

 b Does this carving prove that Greek medicine had not progressed?

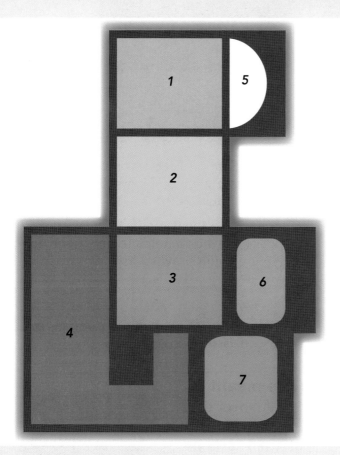

▲ A plan of a Roman bath house.

1 *Frigidarium* (cold room)

2 *Tepidarium* (warm room)

3 *Caldarium* (hot room)

4 *Praefurnium* (furnace room)

5 Cold plunge bath

6 Hot steam bath

7 Hot water tank

1 a What were the five Roman ideas about bad health?

b What did the Romans do to make a public health system?

2 a Why do you think the Romans wanted their soldiers to be healthy?

b How did they make sure their soldiers stayed healthy?

3 Why was Galen so important in the history of medicine?

4 Which of the following was the most important in helping medicine develop in:

a the Greek period

b the Roman period?

● the power of governments

● the brilliance of individuals

● transport and communications

● religion.

CHAPTER 6

THE FALL OF THE ROMAN EMPIRE IN THE WEST

The Roman Empire – East and West

By the 4th century AD the Roman Empire was weak. It split into two.
The Eastern Empire was ruled from Byzantium. The Western Empire was ruled from Rome. But soon Rome was invaded by tribes from other parts of Europe, such as the Huns, Goths and Vandals. Britain was invaded by the Anglo-Saxons.

Source A

Snapped rooftrees, towers fallen, the work of Giants, the stonesmiths, mouldereth.

And the wielders and workmen? Earthgrip holds them – gone, long gone, fast in gravesgrasp.

▲ Part of an Anglo-Saxon poem, *The Ruin*. It describes a ruined Roman city.

What the fall of the Roman Empire meant

The Romans left Britain in about AD 410. All over the Roman Empire government had been strong. There had been good roads, big towns, clean water systems, sewage systems and strong laws so people felt safe. When the Romans became weak all this broke down. No one mended the roads or the water pipes. The towns fell down. The laws broke down. People did not feel safe. Local kings tried to keep some sort of law and order but there was a lot of fighting. People went back to living in mud huts and growing their own food.

The loss of learning

Within a hundred years no one was left who knew how to build stone roads, aqueducts, bridges or public baths. Libraries fell down. Books were lost. People could not learn about medicine, mathematics or anything else. Historians often called this period of time in Western Europe, the Dark Ages.

Source B

When you see a dung beetle digging, catch it and some earth. Wave it about and say:
Remedium facio ad ventris dolorum [help stomach ache].
Then throw the beetle away, over your back, without looking.
When someone comes to you with stomach ache, hold the stomach between your hands. They will be well. This will work for a year after catching the beetle.

▲ A Saxon cure for stomach ache, around the 6th century AD.

Source C

Catch a frog when neither moon or sun is shining. Cut off the hind legs. Wrap them in deerskin. Put the frog's left leg to the patient's gouty left foot and he will certainly be cured.

▲ A cure used by 'Gilbert', a doctor working in the early 11th century.

Source D

▲ A reconstruction of a Saxon home.

▼ The Dark Ages timeline.

D 350	AD 400		AD 500	AD 600	AD 700	AD 800	AD 900	AD 1000	AD 1050

Last Western Roman Emperor overthrown

The Ruin written

'Gilbert' working as a doctor

Fall of Rome to the Goths

Last Roman troops leave Britain

Roman Empire spilt into two

QUESTIONS

1 Read Source A and **What the fall of the Roman Empire meant.**

Who do you think the 'Giants' were in Source A?

2 Read Source B.

a Read Source H on page 26. Do you think this cure for chest trouble is more sensible than the cure for stomach ache in Source B? Explain your answer.

b Look at the date of Source H on page 26 and the date of Source B. Read the box called **Progress and Regress**. Was there progress or regress in medicine between the time of the Greeks and the time of the Saxons?

PROGRESS AND REGRESS

In this book we are looking at one aspect of human society, medicine, through time. We need to be careful how we use the technical words which describe the story. **Progress** means something moving forward. In our context this means getting better, improving. **Regress** means something moving backwards, in our case, getting worse.

CHAPTER 7

ISLAMIC MEDICINE

7.1 Islamic civilization

The Roman Empire in the West collapsed by AD 500. The Eastern Empire survived and kept Greek and Roman learning alive. Some of this learning was brought to the Middle East.

Muhammad

Meanwhile a new civilization grew up in the Middle East. It was based on the religious teachings of Muhammad. He was born in AD 570.

Islam

The followers of Muhammad were called Muslims. The new religion Muhammad founded was called Islam.

The *Qur'an*

The Holy Book of Islam is the *Qur'an*. It tells every Muslim, rich and poor, men, women and children how to live their lives.

Muslims also had to follow the 'wise sayings' of Muhammad collected in the *Hadith*.

The Islamic Empire

Muhammad died in AD 632. Then Islam was ruled by caliphs. Muslims were told to spread Muhammad's teachings. By AD 1000 the caliphs ruled a huge empire. It stretched from Spain in the west to the River Indus in the east. People in the Islamic Empire all spoke Arabic and Islam was the most important religion.

Wealth and learning

The caliphs grew rich through trade. They built beautiful cities such as Baghdad and Cairo. In these cities they built schools and universities. They also built mosques in which to worship. They built public baths because the *Qur'an* said that keeping clean was important.

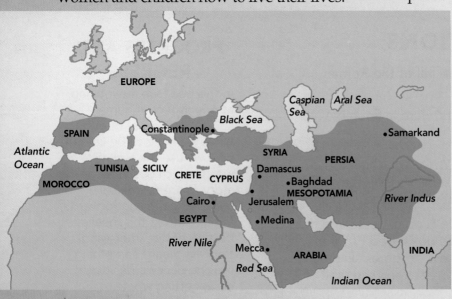

▲ Islamic influence in about AD 1000.

QUESTIONS

1 Where did Greek and Roman learning survive after the fall of the Roman Empire?

2 a What is the Qur'an?

   b What does it teach?

3 Read **The Islamic Empire**. What united all the people in the Islamic Empire?

Religion and dissection

All religions influence the way people think and behave. Both Christianity and Islam refused to allow the dissection of human bodies. This prevented surgeons from studying the human body in full.

The importance of learning

Islam encouraged learning. Books were so important in the Arabic world that by AD 794 Baghdad had its own paper factory. Arabic doctors learnt from the medical ideas in Greek books and then made their own discoveries.

Treating patients

Both Muslims and Christians thought that diseases could be in the hands of God or Allah. The Islamic *Hadith* told doctors to try to cure patients: 'Oh servant of Allah, use medicine. Allah has not created pain without a remedy for it'.

Keeping clean

The *Qur'an* insisted on cleanliness. Islamic doctors saw how important this was when they treated patients.

Caring for patients

Hospitals were set up to care for the sick. The Cairo hospital was set up in AD 1283. Patients were given money when they left so that they did not have to go straight back to work.

Source A

▲ Caliph Manum (AD 813–33) having a shower, haircut and massage in the bath house of his palace in Baghdad.

Source B

Keep your house and yards clean. Allah does not like dirt and untidiness. Every Muslim must have a bath once a week, when he must wash his head and his whole body.

▲ Adapted from the Islamic book, the *Hadith*.

QUESTIONS

1 Give one example of how the teachings of the Qur'an influenced Islamic medicine.

Causes of diseases

Arab doctors accepted the ideas of Hippocrates and Galen. They used the ideas that they thought worked, such as the idea of the four humours. They accepted the idea of clinical observation.

Drugs and chemistry

The Arabs invented new ways of making medicines, such as **distillation**. They used many drugs including senna, musk and camphor.

Hospitals and doctors

Islamic towns and cities often had several hospitals. Doctors were trained in these hospitals. A doctor who passed his training was given a licence.

Rhazes

Rhazes was a Persian. He was an important doctor in Baghdad in about AD 900. He used the idea of the humours. He also used the idea of observation or watching closely. He was the first doctor to write about the difference between measles and smallpox.

Avicenna

Avicenna was a very important doctor. He wrote a book about medicine called the *Canon of Medicine*. Avicenna used the ideas of Galen. He also added some of his own.

Why was Avicenna's book so important?

Avicenna's book was very important. First, it is a very good book about disease and medicine. Second, the book was translated into Latin. This meant that doctors in Europe could read it. They learnt about the ideas of Galen which had been forgotten in Europe. The *Canon of Medicine* was the main book for training doctors until about 1700.

Source C

▲ Doctors in the Islamic Empire used many herbal medicines. This picture is from a Greek herbal book by Dioscorides that had been translated into Arabic.

Source D

All that is written in books is worth much less than the experience of a wise doctor.

▲ Written by Rhazes in about AD 900.

Source E

Smallpox brings backache, fever, stinging pains, red cheeks and eyes and difficulty with breathing. There is more excitement, sickness and unrest in measles than in smallpox. Aching in the back is less.

▲ From *On Smallpox and Measles*, written by Rhazes in about AD 900.

QUESTIONS

1 Write two sentences about Rhazes to show that Islamic medicine continued from Greek medicine.

2 How did an Islamic doctor learn his job?

Anaesthetics

Surgeons soaked a sponge in a mixture of narcotics such as hashish and **opium**. They put the sponge over the patient's face.

Source F

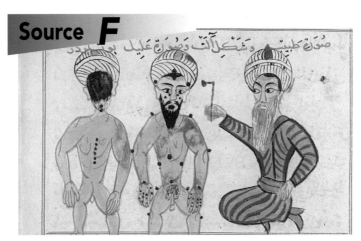

▲ Arab doctors used cautery. A hot iron was pressed on a wound to seal it and prevent infection from entering it.

Abulcasis

The greatest surgeon was Abulcasis who was born in Spain in about AD 936. He was a careful man. He told surgeons to work out what they were going to do before they cut into someone.

He also warned that Allah was watching and that a surgeon should never operate to make money.

Abulcasis wrote about amputations, taking stones out of the bladder, setting broken bones and many other operations. He also wrote about sewing wounds up.

External surgery

Most Arab surgeons were much more willing to do surgery that did not mean opening out the body. They did eye operations (removing cataracts and tumours).

Source G

I saw an Arab doctor who was treating a man that had a boil on his leg and a woman whose wits were wandering. The doctor put a poultice on the leg. The boil began to heal. He ordered a fresh diet for the woman.

A European doctor came. He said: This doctor has no idea how to cure people. He sent for an axe and had the man's leg amputated. He died.

He turned to the woman and said 'the devil has got into your brain.' He sent for a razor and exposed her brain. He rubbed it with salt. She died also.

▲ Written in about 1150 by a Muslim who fought in the Crusades in the Middle East.

QUESTIONS

1 a Does Source G suggest that western medicine was more or less advanced than Islamic medicine?

b Why might we need to be careful about believing this source?

c How does the writing of Abulcasis support Source G?

CHAPTER 8

MEDICINE IN THE MIDDLE AGES

8.1 Western Europe in the Middle Ages

When the Roman Empire broke up Europe became divided into many small countries. The Christian religion was the only thing these countries had in common. They all looked up to the Pope as head of the Christian Church. All the church services were in Latin – the language the Romans had used.

For 400 years Europe muddled along. Then some countries, such as England, became more united and stronger. Islamic countries in the Middle East also became stronger. The Christians were afraid of the power of Islam. This led to wars (known as the Crusades) between Christians and Muslims.

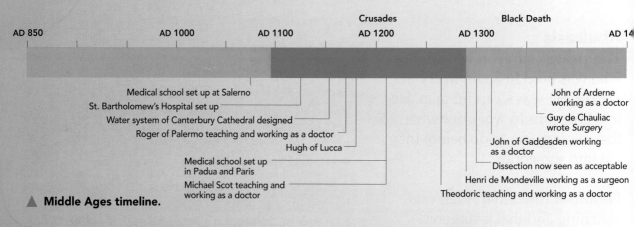

▲ **Middle Ages timeline.**

AD 850 — AD 1000 — AD 1100 — Crusades / AD 1200 — Black Death / AD 1300 — AD 14

- Medical school set up at Salerno
- St. Bartholomew's Hospital set up
- Water system of Canterbury Cathedral designed
- Roger of Palermo teaching and working as a doctor
- Hugh of Lucca
- Medical school set up in Padua and Paris
- Michael Scot teaching and working as a doctor
- Theodoric teaching and working as a doctor
- Henri de Mondeville working as a surgeon
- Dissection now seen as acceptable
- John of Gaddesden working as a doctor
- Guy de Chauliac wrote *Surgery*
- John of Arderne working as a doctor

8.2 Beliefs about the causes of disease

Beliefs about the causes of disease in the Middle Ages

1 Some people believed that magic and evil spirits caused disease.
2 Some people believed that the planets caused disease.
3 Some people, like monks, used the theory of the four humours to look for the cause of disease.
4 The Church said that God sometimes sent disease to punish a person.

Source A

I allowed only red things to be about his bed, by which I cured him, without leaving a trace of the smallpox pustules on him.

▲ **Written by John of Gaddesden, Edward II's doctor, in 1314. He is describing how he had cured Edward's son of smallpox.**

Source B

For scrofula tumours and boils, use the herb scelerat softened and mixed with pig dung.

◄ From a 13th century medical book. Scrofula was a form of tuberculosis.

Treatments

1. Sometimes magical cures were used. For instance, a herbal drink with a bitter taste might drive out an evil spirit.
2. Some doctors carried a book about the planets around with them, to help them discover what was wrong with their patients. This book was called a *Vademecum*. It had charts to show how to tell what was wrong by looking at the sick person's urine. It also told how and when to bleed a patient.
3. Some monks and some doctors used herbs to treat disease. They worked to get the sick person's body back into balance again.
4. Many people prayed to God for help. Some went on **pilgrimages** to places like Canterbury to ask the saints to help them get well.

Source C

When scrofula comes to a head cut so that the pus comes out. If they harden for a month or more, or if the patient is a boy use this oil.

At the declining of the moon make eleven poultices of iris and soft radish, use one a day. Bleed the patient at least once.

If all this is not sufficient, surgery must be used. Hold the patient's throat, cut the skin and pull the scrofula out with a hook.

▲ From a 14th century book by the doctor, Roger of Salerno.

Source D

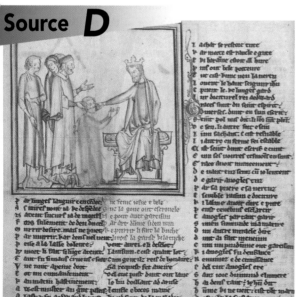

◄ Edward the Confessor touches a man to cure him from scrofula. Many kings and queens of England were believed to be able to cure scrofula.

QUESTIONS

1. a Read **Beliefs about the causes of disease in the Middle Ages** and **Treatments**. Write down the four beliefs. Next to each belief write a possible treatment.

   b Which of the four beliefs are new? Which ones are old?

8.3 Growing professionalism

The Romans left Britain in the 5th century. For the next few hundred years Europe muddled along. By about AD 1000 things began to change.

Teaching doctors

The first medical school was at Salerno in Italy. The teachers used the books of Hippocrates and Galen. (Many of these books had been saved by the Arab doctors. Now they were translated back into Latin). The use of these books led to three things.

- Teachers began to teach clinical observation again.
- Teachers began to teach more about keeping clean again.
- Teachers began to teach the theory of the four humours again.

However, the books of Hippocrates and Galen were the only books used. Young doctors were taught that everything in them was true.

Higher standards

The Holy Roman Emperor was very impressed by the teaching at Salerno. So, in 1221 he passed a law saying that only doctors trained there could treat patients. (This only applied to rich people who were sick!) However, it was the first time that a standard was fixed for training doctors.

Other medical schools

Other medical schools started, such as Bologna and Paris. By the 14th century there were many places in Europe where doctors could train. More and more doctors were trained. Some began to question the ideas of Hippocrates and Galen. New ideas were put forward. One of these was using the colour of urine to help to diagnose what was happening to a sick person. Even the Christian Church moved with the times. Doctors were allowed to see dissection done so that they could learn more about the human body.

Source E

When you are asked if a sick person will get better or die, look at his star sign.

Also examine the moon for the sick person because it can tell us something too.

Then check the tenth house and its ruling sign, since they signify health and medicine.

Do the same for the sixth house, since they signify illness. Then the eighth house, since they signify death for the sick. Then see the fourth house and its lord, since this signifies the end of all the others.

▲ From a book by Michael Scot, a teacher at the medical school in Salerno.

Urine and health

One of the most widely accepted of the new ideas was that the colour and smell of urine could help diagnose sickness. Urine should be clear, pale yellow and not smelly. Strong sweet smells or ammonia smells were a bad sign. So was a dark or cloudy colour.

◀ A urine chart from 1506. They were in use much earlier.
The use of the colour of urine to diagnose disease was a new idea that became widely accepted.

8.4 Ordinary people

Rich people

The books of Hippocrates and Galen were still the main books that teachers used in the medical schools. The doctors who trained at the medical schools treated rich people. So only the rich came into contact with the ideas of Hippocrates and Galen, or any of the new ideas.

Ordinary people in the country

Most people lived in the country. They were not rich. If they were ill they went on treating themselves and their families as they had done for hundreds of years. They used herbs or magical cures. Sometimes there were women and men in the village who had learnt about herbs and healing. Often sick people turned to them for help. These people did not write anything down so we do not know much about them.

Women

There is some evidence that the medical school at Salerno trained women as well as men. However, more and more women were being pushed out of medicine. They were only really accepted as **midwives** and healers.

Source G

▲ A woman delivering a baby by *caesarean section.*

► A lecturer reads from a book while his assistant dissects a body.

Barber-surgeons and surgeons

Barber-surgeons cut people's hair. They also did some surgery. They often learnt from their fathers and were the only sort of surgeons that poor people could afford.

Surgeons had medical training. But the job of a surgeon was hard work and very messy. Most doctors did not want to be surgeons. There were few well trained surgeons in the Middle Ages.

Learning surgery

Look at Source I. By about 1300 dissection was allowed in medical schools. In this picture a teacher is reading from a book on the human body by Galen. His assistant is cutting up the body. The assistant's job was to find the things that were in Galen's book.

If he did not find the things Galen wrote about then the teacher said that he had messed up the dissection. Galen could not be wrong.

Pain and infection

Pain and infection were the main problems of surgery. One or two surgeons tried to dull the pain with drugs (see Source K). Others tried to deal with infection by washing wounds in wine (we now know that this is an antiseptic). Nothing seems to have worked well enough for all surgeons to use it.

War surgery

In the early Middle Ages wounded soldiers were looked after by other soldiers or healers. Later, armies took surgeons with them when they went to war.

Successful operations

Practice in war made surgeons more skilled at treating broken bones, removing arrows and **cauterising** wounds.

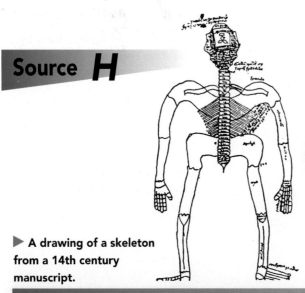

► A drawing of a skeleton from a 14th century manuscript.

It is dangerous for a surgeon who is not famous to operate in any new way.

▲ Written by Henri de Mondeville (1260–1320), a master surgeon at the University of Bologna.

Source K

Take the gall of a boar, and three spoonfuls each of juice of hemlock, wild briony, lettuce, opium poppy, henbane and vinegar.

Mix together and add three spoonfuls of the mixture to a bottle of wine or ale.

The man to be operated on should drink the whole bottle by a warm fire. He will fall asleep and then can be operated on.

▲ A recipe for an anaesthetic from John of Arderne, a well known English surgeon in 1376.

QUESTIONS

1 Read **Barber-surgeons and surgeons** on page 52. Why did some doctors not want to be surgeons?

2 Read **Learning surgery** and the caption of Source I. Was medieval anatomy better than Galen's anatomy? Write out the statement below that most agrees with what you think.
   - It was better because teachers could dissect bodies.
   - It was not better because teachers let assistants dissect the bodies.
   - It was not better because teachers said Galen was right even if the assistant cutting up the body found something different.

8.6 Public health

The Romans had been very well organized. They had piped clean water to the towns. This had made it easy for people to keep clean.

But in the Middle Ages governments were not as well organized as the Romans. So there was not much clean water in towns.

Towns

In the Middle Ages towns were run by groups of men who formed a local council. They raised money to run the town.

Usually there was not enough money to pipe water to everyone, or to make drains to take the dirty water away.

Source L

The lane called Ebbegate used to be a right of way until it was closed up by Thomas at Wytte and William de Hockele who built latrines which stuck out from the walls of the houses. From these latrines human filth falls out on to the heads of passers-by.

▲ Evidence given in a court case heard in London in 1321.

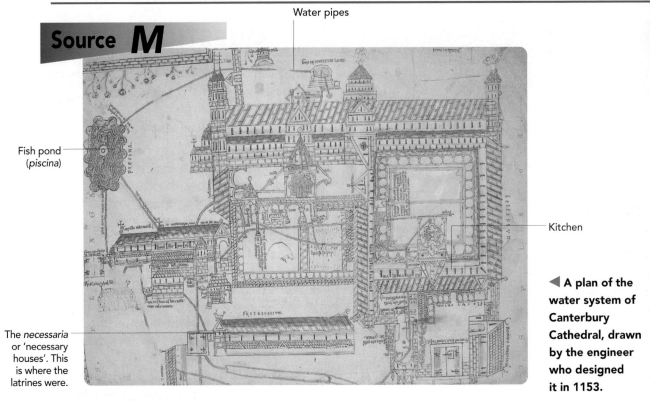

Water pipes

Fish pond (*piscina*)

Kitchen

The *necessaria* or 'necessary houses'. This is where the latrines were.

◄ A plan of the water system of Canterbury Cathedral, drawn by the engineer who designed it in 1153.

What happened to the rubbish and sewage?

Sometimes people built toilets over a stream or even had a **cesspit** under the house. Streams clogged up with sewage and stank. Cesspits overflowed. Some people put their rubbish and sewage in the street. Councils sometimes passed laws against this but no one took much notice. The only time that people cleaned up was when serious disease broke out.

Monasteries

Monasteries were often rich and well organized. They often piped clean water from a river and built drains to take the sewage far from the monastery. Canterbury Cathedral (also a monastery) had a complicated water system.

Canterbury Cathedral

The water from the river was piped through five tanks to make sure it was clean. Water from washing was used to flush the toilets which were built away from the main buildings. Monks washed their hands and faces before meals and at other times.

All the streets are so badly paved that they get wet easily. This happens a lot because of the cattle carrying water, and the rain. Evil smelling mud is formed which seems to last all year round.

▲ Written by a visitor to Winchester in 1286.

▲ An illustration of a water seller, from the 14th century *Lutterell Psalter*.

Hospitals

By about 1200 there were a few hospitals in Europe. Most were set up by monks. Not all of them had doctors or surgeons. They did not treat sickness. They just made the patients as comfortable as they could. Apart from this there were a few hospitals for lepers (people suffering from **leprosy**), and other hospitals for women having babies.

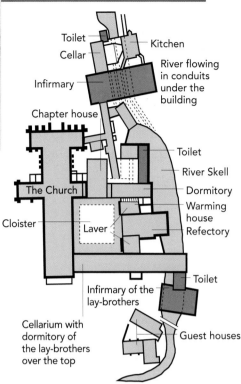

▲ Fountains Abbey, a monastery in Yorkshire, showing the water supply and drainage.

8.7 The Black Death

The Black Death: 1347–49

The Black Death was also called the **plague**. It came to Europe in 1347. Within a year it had reached Britain. People fell ill with a temperature and soon lumps (buboes) appeared in the armpit or groin. The buboes went black. After a few days the person either died or began to get better.

What caused the Black Death?

We now know there were two main sorts of plague. Pneumonic plague was spread by coughs and sneezing. Bubonic plague was caused by flea bites. The fleas lived on black rats. Rats were common in the dirty towns and on the ships of that time. The fleas spread quickly from the rats to other animals and then to people.

QUESTIONS

1   There were lots of water sellers (like the man in Source O) in towns in the Middle Ages. They sold clean water from rivers or pumps. Does this show progress or regress in the history of medicine?

2   Were monasteries better organized than towns? Use sources L to N to support your answer.

What did people at the time think?

No one at the time knew what caused the plague. The sources below show some of the things people thought caused it.

None of the reasons given, however, fully explained how the plague was spread.

How many people died?

No one knew how to stop the plague. In 1348 and 1349, between one third and one half of the population of Britain died. As many as 2.5 million people might have died from the disease. Sometimes whole villages were wiped out.

Source P

Some people believed the cause of the Black Death was poison. It was either the Jews, or cripples or nobles poisoning people. If someone was carrying a powder or ointment people made him swallow it for fear it might be poisonous.

But the truth is that there were two causes. The general cause was the close position of the three great planets, Saturn, Jupiter and Mars on 24th March 1345, in the 14th degree of Aquarius. The particular cause in each person was the state of the body – bad digestion, weakness or blockage.

▲ From *On Surgery*, written in 1363, by Guy de Chauliac a French doctor.

Source R

Whoever touched the sick or dead was infected and died. I, waiting for death 'till it come, have put these things in writing.

▲ An Irish friar who died from the Black Death in 1349.

Source S

The plague comes from the ground or the air or both together.

As we see a privy [toilet] which makes the air dirty next to a chamber.

Sometimes it comes from dead bodies or stagnant water.

▲ Written in 1485 by the Bishop of Aarhus in Denmark.

Source Q

Many people think that the Jews did not poison the water. They only confessed because they were tortured.

Wise people think the plague was caused by an earthquake which let out bad vapours into the springs and wells. Many Jews are doctors and know how to avoid the plague.

▲ From a book about the history of Switzerland by Glig Tshudi, written in about 1560. He used many reports from 1349.

Source T

▲ A doctor with a plague victim. He is carrying a pomander to keep off bad smells. His assistants carry tapers to clear bad air.

QUESTIONS

1 Look at Sources P, Q, S, T and U. Copy out any of the causes listed below that people believed at the time.

Poisoning/the planets/dogs/bad smells/having teeth out/touching dead bodies/bad digestion/weaknesses.

2 Are any of the ideas about causes of disease (in the list above) old ideas? Where in this book have you met them before?

Cures

People in the Middle Ages could not stop the plague from spreading. They could not treat it. However, they tried both spiritual and physical cures.

Source U

The filth lying in the streets of the city and its suburbs must be removed with all speed to places far distant.

The city and suburbs are to be kept clean so that no further deaths may arise from such smells.

▲ An order sent by King Edward III to the Lord Mayor of London, in 1349.

Source V

The swellings should be softened with figs and cooked onions mixed with yeast and butter, then opened and treated like ulcers.

▲ From *On Surgery* by Guy de Chauliac.

Source W

The reek of plague sores poisons the air because the humours of the body are infected. In times of plague people should not crowd together, because someone may be infected.

Avoid all four stinks – the stable, stinking fields or streets, dead bodies and stinking water. Clean your house. Make a fire. Burn herbs, such as bay and juniper, to clear the air.

▲ Written in 1485 by the Bishop of Aarhus in Denmark.

▲ Flagellants whipping themselves. These people thought the Black Death was sent by God because people were sinful.

Source Y

About Michaelmas 1349, over six hundred men came to London from Flanders. They wore clothes from the waist down, but otherwise were bare. They wore a cap with a red cross.

Each had a whip with three tails with nails in them. They marched one behind the other and whipped themselves till they bled.

They were singing and chanting as they went.

They would throw themselves on the ground three times in turn, stretching their arms out like they were on the cross. Then they would take turns whipping the one lying on the ground.

▲ A description of the flagellants in London by a witness.

QUESTIONS

1   a Look at Source W on page 57. What idea in this source was first put forward by the Greeks?

    b What are the four stinks in Source W?

2   Read Sources U and V on page 57. How do they suggest curing people who had the plague?

3   a Look at Sources X and Y. How do they support each other?

    b Are there any ways in which X and Y contradict each other?

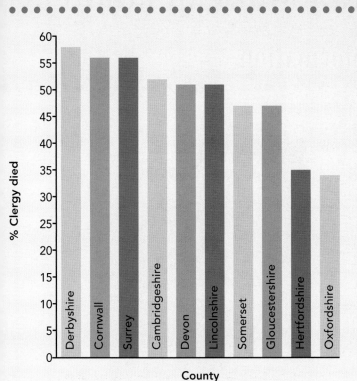

▲ This bar graph shows the percentage of clergy who died in various counties of England during the outbreak of the Black Death in 1348–9.

1 What do we now know about the Black Death that people did not know in 1348?

2 Could people have stopped the spread of the Black Death if they had known what caused it? Explain your answer.

3 Look at the graph. Does the graph prove that the Black Death had a devastating impact on 14th century England? Explain your answer.

Medicine in the Middle Ages

Copy and complete the chart below. Two boxes have been filled in as examples.

Factors	Question	Answer	Don't know
Science and Technology	How much did they know about the body and the world?		
War	How did war affect treatment?		✓
Religion	How did religion affect treatment and learning?		
Government	How well organized were they?		
Communications	How much contact was there between different countries?	Contact with Arab countries brought Greek and Roman books back to Europe, together with new Arabic ideas.	
Chance	Did unexpected things happen?		

CHAPTER 9

MEDICINE IN EARLY MODERN EUROPE

9.1 Renaissance and Reformation

The Middle Ages had been a time of slow change. Between 1430 and 1700 (usually called the Early Modern period) things changed more quickly.

Renaissance – from 1430

Renaissance means rebirth. From about 1430 there was a rebirth of old ideas. People looked back to the ideas of the Greeks and Romans. They read Greek and Roman books. They wanted to learn everything the Greeks and Romans had learned. This was the rebirth of interest and learning. They had new ideas, too, about how the world worked. Most of these ideas were based on careful observation.

Source A

◀ A drawing of a foetus from a medieval book for midwives.

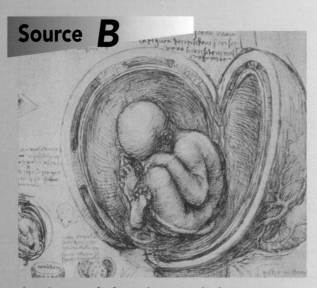

Source B

▲ A drawing of a foetus by Leonardo da Vinci. He dissected the body of a woman who died in pregnancy.

Art in the Renaissance

Artists said that pictures had to look real. Artists went to see human bodies dissected so that they knew exactly what a body was like. Some artists drew so well their pictures helped doctors to understand the way bodies were put together.

The Reformation

The Reformation went hand in hand with the Renaissance. People read and thought more. They wanted more change. Many people said that the Church was too powerful. They wanted to change the Church.

Printing

In the Middle Ages books were written by hand. They took months or years to make. They were so expensive they were kept chained up in libraries. But Johannes Gutenberg changed this. He printed the first books in Europe in 1454. Soon printed books were rolling off the printing presses. Many more people could now read about the ideas of the Greeks and Romans, or the new ideas on medicine and religion.

Medicine

The new printed books, with their clear pictures by famous artists, made a huge difference to medicine. Soon doctors were questioning the old ideas about the human body.

Paracelsus

Paracelsus was typical of the new questioning. He was the town doctor and lecturer at Basel University. In 1527 he invited students, barber-surgeons and anyone who was interested to come and listen to him. He started his first lecture by burning a pile of books. These were books by Galen and Avicenna. Paracelsus said: *'Galen is a liar and a fake. Avicenna (a famous Arab doctor) is a kitchen master. They are good for nothing. You will not need them. Reading never made a doctor. Patients are the only books.'*

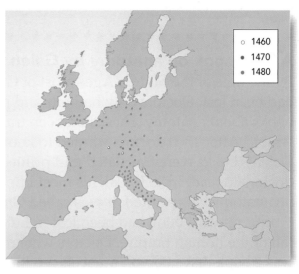

▲ **The spread of printers' workshops, 1460–80.**

○ 1460
● 1470
● 1480

QUESTIONS

1 Read **Art in the Renaissance**. How did changes in art help doctors?

2 Read **Paracelsus.**

  a Who was Paracelsus?

  b What did he say about Galen?

  c What did he say about Avicenna?

  d Why was his lecture important in the history of medicine?

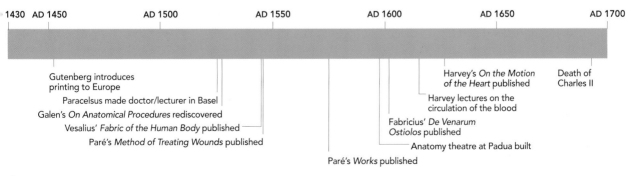

1430 AD 1450   AD 1500   AD 1550   AD 1600   AD 1650   AD 1700

Gutenberg introduces printing to Europe
Paracelsus made doctor/lecturer in Basel
Galen's *On Anatomical Procedures* rediscovered
Vesalius' *Fabric of the Human Body* published
Paré's *Method of Treating Wounds* published
Paré's *Works* published
Fabricius' *De Venarum Ostiolos* published
Anatomy theatre at Padua built
Harvey lectures on the circulation of the blood
Harvey's *On the Motion of the Heart* published
Death of Charles II

▲ **Early Modern medicine 1430–1700.**

9.2 Vesalius and anatomy

A new book on anatomy by Galen

By the time of the Middle Ages most of Galen's books had been lost. Doctors only had bits and pieces of his books about anatomy. These had been translated from Arabic. After 1500 doctors wanted to know more. So Galen's books were translated and printed for all doctors to read. In 1531 Galen's most important book on anatomy was printed. It was called *On Anatomical Procedures*. This book had been lost in Europe since the fall of the Roman Empire. Doctors were delighted. Here was a book that said you must start with the skeleton. You must look carefully at the human body.

Vesalius

Vesalius was born into a medical family in Brussels in 1514. He studied medicine at home, at Louvain and in Paris. He was fascinated by human dissection (which was allowed). But he really wanted to boil up a human body and get a skeleton (which was not allowed).

How Vesalius got a skeleton

Vesalius went to a gibbet outside the town of Louvain. On the gibbet was a dried up body of a criminal. All the flesh had gone. The bones were held together by the ligaments.

'I climbed the stake and pulled off the femur from the hip bone. The shoulder blades together with the arms and hands followed, although the fingers of one hand, both knee caps and one foot were missing.

Later I allowed myself to be shut out of the city in the evening in order to obtain the trunk, which was firmly held by a chain. The next day I transported the bones home through another gate in the city.'

Source C

As poles to tents, and walls to houses, so are bones to living creatures.

▲ From *On Anatomical Procedures*, written by Galen in about AD 200, lost until 1531.

Source D

I would let him cut me as often as he has cut man or other animal [except when eating].

▲ Vesalius on Johannes Guinter. He means Guinter had done little surgery or dissection.

Source E

I yield to none in my devotion and reverence to Galen.

▲ Vesalius, answering to criticism that he was against Galen.

Vesalius at Padua

In 1537 Vesalius went to Padua in Italy. He taught surgery and anatomy.

Teaching anatomy

Vesalius taught anatomy by doing his own dissections. This was a change because teachers had usually let an assistant do them. Vesalius made another change too. He published drawings of his dissections. He said these drawings would help students to understand what they were seeing during a dissection lesson.

The Tabulae Sex

In 1538 Vesalius published the *Tabulae Sex*. It was made up of six large sheets of drawings. In some of the drawings Vesalius shows the human liver just as Galen described it – with five lobes. But Galen had not been allowed to cut up humans, only animals. In fact animals have five lobed livers, humans only have two lobes. One of Vesalius' drawings shows a two lobed liver. Vesalius was beginning to question what Galen said.

Venesection

Venesection is the bleeding of sick people. Some doctors said only a small amount of blood should be taken. It should be taken on the opposite side of the body from the side that was sick. However, Vesalius wanted to get back to the ideas of Hippocrates and Galen who suggested taking more blood. Also, they had not said anything about which side of the body to take it from. Vesalius did drawings of the veins and gave reasons why the ideas of Hippocrates and Galen were right.

Source F

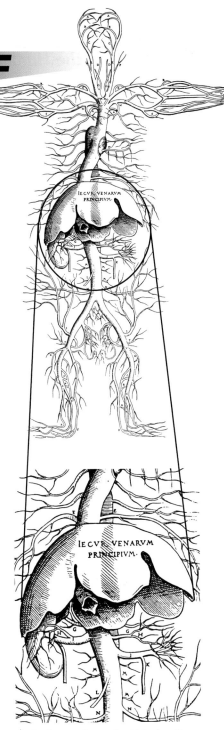

▲ A picture from the *Tabulae Sex*, by Vesalius published in 1538. It shows the ideas of Galen. The liver (see detail) is shown as a five lobed organ as Galen described it. This is the shape of an animal liver, not a human liver, which has only two lobes.

The Fabric of the Human Body 1543

This was Vesalius' great book on anatomy. The drawings were by first class artists. The publication of this book was an important moment in the history of medicine. Here are some of the reasons why it was so important.

Why *The Fabric of the Human Body* was important

1 The pictures were drawn from real human bodies.
2 Vesalius starts with the outside and works in. The part on the muscles starts with a picture of a body with the skin removed. This shows the surface muscles. Each picture after that shows deeper and deeper muscles.
3 Vesalius corrected some of Galen's mistakes in anatomy.
4 It was a new way of teaching – public dissection backed up with pictures.
5 It was a new type of book. Vesalius used the pictures to tell the story.
6 Vesalius spent months making sure all the wood blocks that were cut to print the pictures were absolutely correct to the smallest detail.
7 Vesalius' book was printed (not hand written) so there were lots of copies. Soon every medical school in Europe had a copy of *The Fabric of the Human Body*.

Vesalius' later life

Although at the time some old fashioned doctors disagreed with him, Vesalius' ideas changed the way anatomy was taught. His work was based on human dissection and, therefore, hard to argue with.

Vesalius wrote other books and became a doctor at the court of the Emperor, Charles V. He left the court in 1564 to go back to teaching in Padua but he died before he arrived there.

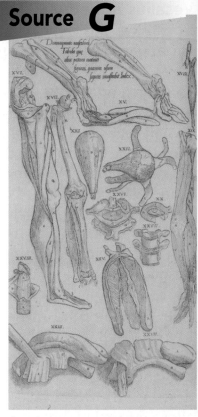

Source G

▲ The 16th picture from Vesalius' description of the muscles. Notice the letters and numbers which link the pictures to Vesalius' words.

ANDREAE VESALII
BRVXELLENSIS, SCHOLAE
medicorum Patauinæ profefforis, de
Humani corporis fabrica
Libri feptem.

▲ The front page of *The Fabric of the Human Body.* Vesalius is doing the dissection outside. This was common at the time. Wooden stands were built so as many people as possible could watch.

QUESTIONS

1 What two changes did Vesalius make in the teaching of anatomy?

2 What organ in the human body did Vesalius realise that Galen had described incorrectly?

3 Which do you think was the most important book in helping to bring about developments in medicine:

  a *The Tabulae Sex*

  b *The Fabric of the Human Body?*
    Explain your answer.

4 Read TRENDS AND TURNING POINTS. Was *The Fabric of the Human Body* a trend or a turning point? Explain your answer.

TRENDS AND TURNING POINTS

A **trend** is a gradual change. It is made up of a series of events.

A **turning point** is a quick change. It may be just one event. Afterwards, things are never the same.

9.3 Ambroise Paré

Barber-surgeons
Ambroise Paré was the son of a barber-surgeon. Barber-surgeons were looked down on by doctors.

To Paris and the army
Paré went to Paris to train as a barber-surgeon in 1523. Although he became a good surgeon he did not have the money to take the examinations. He joined the French army. Since France was often at war, he became an expert in gunshot wounds. In 1545 he wrote a book about how to treat gunshot wounds.

Surgeon to the king
In 1552 Paré became surgeon to the king of France. He wrote more books. But the Faculty of Physicians attacked him. They said he was ignorant. (He was only a barber-surgeon.) They said that the Faculty had to approve all books published. However, the king was on Paré's side so his books carried on selling.

The *Apology and Treatise of Ambroise Paré* – 1585
In 1585 Paré wrote his own life story. It was called the *Apology and Treatise of Ambroise Paré*. He wrote about the cases he had treated. He also wrote to explain the way he worked. Sources J, K and L are from Paré's book.

Source I

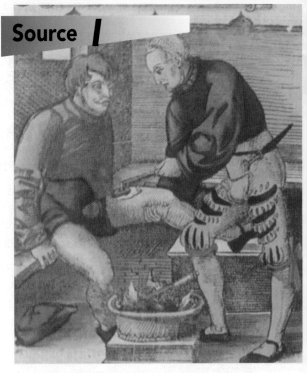

▲ This picture shows the old treatment of gunshot wounds. Gunshot wounds were thought to be poisonous. They were treated by burning with a red hot iron (cautery) or they were filled with boiling oil.

Source J

Dare you say you will teach me surgery, you who have never come out of your study? Surgery is learned by the eye and the hands. I can perform surgical operations which you cannot do, because you have never left your study or the schools. Diseases are not to be cured by talking. You do nothing else but chatter in a chair.

[Later Paré describes a battlefield covered with many dead men and horses]. So many blue and green flies rose from them they hid the sun; where they settled they infested the air and brought the plague with them.

▲ From the *Apology and Treatise of Ambroise Paré*, 1585. He is writing about a lecturer who criticised his work.

I had read that wounds made with weapons of fire were poisoned. They should be treated by cauterizing them with oil scalding hot mixed with a little treacle. Knowing it would cause great pain, I wanted to know what other surgeons did. They put on the oil as hot as possible. I took courage to do as they did.

Eventually I ran out of oil. I was forced to use an ointment made from yolks of eggs, oil of roses and turpentine.

That night I could not sleep. I was afraid what would happen because the wounds had not had burning oil. I rose early. To my surprise I found those to whom I gave my ointment feeling little pain and their wounds without inflammation or swelling. Whereas the others, on whom I used boiling oil, were feverish, with great pain and swelling about the edges of the wound.

Then I decided with myself never so cruelly to burn poor men wounded with gunshot.

▲ The story of how Paré discovered a new treatment for gunshot wounds.

Amputation
Let us suppose that a foot needs to be amputated. Let the patient be fed with meats, yolks of eggs, and bread toasted and dipped in wine to [keep him strong].

Place the patient as fit. Draw the muscles back and tie with a ligature....When you have made your ligature cut the flesh to the bone with a sharp well-cutting knife or with a crooked knife.

When you come to the bone cut it with a little saw. Then you must smooth the edge of the bone that the saw has made rough.

Bleeding
Let it bleed a little, then tie up the veins and arteries so that the course of the flowing blood may be stopped. This may be done by taking hold of the vessels with your Crow's Beak, which looks like this:

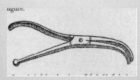

I used to stop the bleeding another way, of which I am ashamed, but what should I do? I had observed my masters who used hot irons. This kind of treatment could not but bring great pain to the patient. And truly of those that were burnt, only about a third of them recovered. I entreat all surgeons to leave this old and too cruel way and embrace this new.

▲ From *Of Amputations*, which appeared in Paré's *Works*, 1575.

Some years ago a certain gentleman had a bezoar stone. These stones were thought to be an antidote [cure] for all poisons. He bragged about it to King Charles. The king asked me whether there could be an antidote for all poisons. I said no because all poisons were different. I also said that it was an easy matter to test the stone on someone condemned to be hanged. The idea pleased the king.

There was a cook who was to be hanged for stealing two silver dishes. The king asked the cook whether he would take the poison and then the antidote. He could then go free. The cook cheerfully agreed.

So he was given poison and then some bezoar. After a while he began to vomit and move his bowels, and to cry out that his inward parts were burnt with fire.

After an hour I went to him. He was on the ground like a beast, with his tongue thrust forth out of his mouth, his eyes fiery, with cold sweats, and blood flowing from his ears, nose, mouth, anus and penis. At length he died in great torment seven hours after he took the poison.

▲ From *Of Bezoar* part of Paré's *Works*, 1575.

The importance of Paré

Paré was important for two reasons.

1 Paré understood how to test out a theory to see whether it was worth following or not (see Source M). This is at the heart of modern scientific thinking.
2 Paré also wanted to make all his new ideas public. This was so that other doctors could learn from him. The only way that medicine could progress was if doctors learnt from each other.

QUESTIONS

1 Read the caption to Source I on page 66. How were gunshot wounds treated before Paré?

2 Read Source K on page 67.
   a What was Paré's ointment for gunshot wounds made of?
   b What part did **chance** play in Paré's discovery of a new treatment for gunshot wounds? Choose the best sentence from the ones below.
   ● He thought boiling oil did not work.
   ● He ran out of boiling oil.
   ● He hated causing pain.

3 Read **Bleeding** in Source L on page 67.
   a How did surgeons stop bleeding before Paré?
   b How did Paré stop bleeding?

4 Read **The importance of Paré**. Give two reasons why Paré is important in the history of medicine.

9.4 William Harvey and the circulation of the blood

Your brain tells you what you see

Is the drawing on the right a vase or the black shapes of two people facing each other? You can see it both ways. This is because our brain decides what we see. This is one of the reasons why doctors dissecting the human body did not immediately see how it worked. They had been taught to see the body through Galen's system, so they saw the things Galen's system made them expect to see.

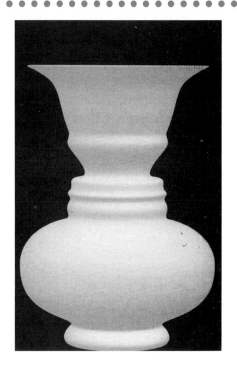

Things you already know

Things you already know help you to understand the world around you. Galen lived in Roman times. He knew about fire, metal smelting and brewing. He used ideas of these things when he thought about how the body worked. William Harvey grew up in a time when pumps were beginning to be used. There were pumps to pump water out of mines. There were also pumps to pump water to put out fires. When Harvey thought about how the heart worked, he could compare it to a pump because he had seen pumps working. Galen had not.

Vesalius changes his mind

At first Vesalius accepted Galen's idea that blood passed from one side of the heart to the other through the septum. Later he disagreed. He said there were definitely no holes. The blood could not pass through the septum.

Realdo Colombo and Geronimo Fabricius

Realdo Colombo worked at Padua after Vesalius. He showed that blood passed from one side of the heart to the other via the lungs. Geronimo Fabricius, another professor of anatomy at Padua, noticed the valves in the veins (1603). Fabricius taught William Harvey who was later to become very famous.

Source N

▶ The anatomy theatre at Padua, built by Fabricius in 1594. Everyone could see what was going on.

William Harvey

Harvey was born in 1578 and studied medicine at Padua. Afterwards he worked in London as a doctor and a teacher of anatomy. He was doctor to James I and Charles I.

Harvey and live hearts

Harvey wanted to find out how the heart worked. He needed live hearts. He worked on animals, but most of them had such fast heartbeats he could not see what was happening. He then worked on frogs because they have a slow heartbeat.

Pumping blood

Harvey saw that each time the heart contracted (became smaller) it pumped out a lot of blood. He worked out how much blood the heart was pumping out. He decided that there was too much blood for it all to be used up, and for the body to make new blood all the time (as Galen said).

Harvey and the circulation of blood

Harvey said there must be a fixed amount of blood in the body. All the blood **circulated** (moved around) the body. It was pumped round by the heart.

Harvey and the valves in veins

Harvey worked out an experiment to show that the little flaps or valves in the veins only allowed blood to flow one way. Now he could show that the blood flowed out from the heart through the arteries. It flowed back through the veins.

Harvey's book about the heart

Harvey published *An Anatomical Treatise on the Motion of the Heart* in 1628. This put forward all his ideas about the blood circulating.

Source O

The two movements of the heart happen so quickly they cannot be seen separately.

It seems to be a single movement. This is like when you pull the trigger of a gun, a flint strikes steel. A spark happens and lights the powder. The flame spreads. The bullet flies out. All these movements happen so quickly you cannot see them separately.

▲ From *An Anatomical Treatise on the Motion of the Heart*, written by William Harvey in 1628.

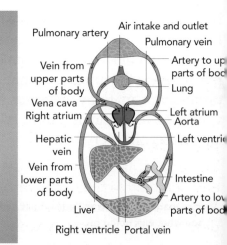

▲ Harvey's physiological system.

Source P

The pump has two valves. One to open when the handle is lifted up and when it is down to shut. The other is to open to let the water out. At the end of the machine a man holds a copper pipe turning it to where the fire shall be.

▲ Salomon de Caus describing a machine for putting out fires, 1615.

Source Q

▲ An illustration from Fabricius' book showing the valves in the veins.

Source R

▲ A pump for putting out fires, 1673.

Source S

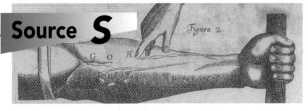

▲ From Harvey's book, 1628. It shows how valves in the veins allow blood to flow in just one direction.

QUESTIONS

1 a Read **Vesalius changes his mind** on page 69. What did Vesalius discover about the heart and blood?

b Read **Realdo Colombo and Geronimo Fabricius**. What did Colombo discover about the heart and blood?

c What did Fabricius discover about veins?

d Who did Fabricius teach?

2 a Read **Harvey and live hearts**. Why did Harvey use the live hearts of frogs?

b Read **Harvey and the circulation of blood**. Write out the three things Harvey said about blood.

c Look at Sources O and R. What two examples of things in everyday life in the 1600s did Harvey use to explain how the heart worked?

3 Look at your answers to all of question 1. Was Harvey's work a development or a change in the history of medicine?

9.5 Treatment

New ideas

There were many new ideas in medicine and anatomy in the Early Modern period. Versalius and Harvey discovered a great deal about how the body worked. Their ideas were more scientific as they were based on close observation.

The choice of treatment

There was little new treatment for ordinary people. The choices were:
● self help
● trained doctors
● apothecaries
● healers.

Self help

Sick people often started by trying to help themselves. Household recipe books have survived. They include recipes for medicines such as a 'syrup for the headache'.

Trained doctors

From 1600 the Royal College of Physicians trained university educated doctors. There were about 50 of these doctors in London in the early 1600s. They charged a lot of money. They wanted to stop anyone else practising medicine.

Apothecaries

Apothecaries mixed medicines. They used many herbs. These could be boiled, dried, pressed or distilled to make pills, syrups and ointments. They also made poultices to put on wounds. They were often called in to treat patients who did not want or could not afford a doctor.

Apothecaries also used chemicals. They usually made these up for doctors. These were doctors who followed the ideas of Paracelsus. He said that the body was made up of chemicals and so chemicals should be used to treat illness. These chemicals included gold and mercury.

Source *T*

▲ *The Doctor's Shop* painted in Holland in the 1660s. The painting was intended to show the range of medicines a doctor or apothecary could provide.

Healers

Healers ranged from herbalists to faith healers. There was about one healer for every 400 people in the countryside. There was about one healer for every 250 people in the towns. There were far more healers than trained doctors or apothecaries.

Local gentry

It was part of the job of the wife of a local gentleman to look after the health of her family and servants. She often looked after the poor as well. She helped with herbs and food.

Women

Trained doctors tried to stop women practising medicine at all. However, women healers and herbalists remained in the countryside. Even in towns women kept the job of midwife. In some towns the council employed women to work as nurses. They did the kind of work that had been done in monasteries and convents in the Middle Ages.

Cures

Different healers used different cures. Here are some listed below:
- praying to god
- giving herbal medicines
- magic spells.

Source U

▲ This shows a woman giving birth. She is being helped by a midwife and friends. The doctors are working out the baby's horoscope.

Source V

Unlicensed doctors are but charlatans. Women, especially, should not practice medicine because they do not have the natural authority of men. Also, they do not have enough capacity for reasoning. They might misdiagnose the disease and kill the patient.

▲ John Cottas, a licensed doctor, wrote this in a book in 1612.

Keeping the body in balance

At the beginning of the Early Modern period almost all healers, apothecaries and doctors worked to keep the body in balance.

A new outlook

During the Early Modern period people became more interested in observation and in experiments. They did not just rely on book learning.

Experimenting

People experimented in many ways, including magic cures. King Charles II reintroduced touching people to cure **scrofula**. (The idea that the king's touch could cure this disease had gone out of fashion in Tudor times). Also Charles II sent for an Irish faith healer so that he could see him perform miracles.

Thomas Sydenham

When Charles II was sick, he sent for Dr Thomas Sydenham. Sydenham said that doctors must observe their sick patients closely. Only by sitting by the bedside and watching could a doctor learn about a disease.

THE ROYAL SOCIETY

The Royal Society was set up in 1662. It was part of the new move to experiment, and King Charles himself was its patron. Samuel Pepys, the famous diarist, was a member and went to many meetings. The Royal Society investigated whatever the members were interested in, including medical and scientific ideas. Pepys went to experiments on the following:

- the effect of heat on glass
- a newly invented musical instrument
- the baking of French bread
- comets
- the effect of poison on dogs, cats and hens
- the effect of a vacuum on a kitten
- the design of coaches
- the human foetus
- the process of felt making
- blood transfusions and circulation
- the refraction of light
- microscopes
- the qualities of gunpowder.

QUESTIONS

1 Read **Trained doctors.**

   a In what way might trained doctors have been a good thing?

   b In what way might trained doctors have been a bad thing?

2 Read **Experimenting.**
   Was Charles II backward looking in his experiments or not? Explain your answer.

Source 1

▲ A painting from 1556 by Peter Bruegel. The purpose of the picture was to make fun of barber-surgeons.

Source 2

Paré's use of ligatures was not new. It was not popular because many surgeons believed it was risky. In one way they were right. Paré's ligatures stopped bleeding. However, they were dangerous because the threads could take infection into the wound.

Source 3

Paré made improvements in surgery. However, most surgeons continued to use the cautery iron and worked in filthy conditions. The full benefit of using ligatures was not seen until Lister showed how infection spread.

◀▲ Extracts from a recent book on the history of medicine, commenting on Paré's work.

● ●

Early Modern medicine

Copy and complete the chart below. Two boxes have been filled in as examples.

Factor	Question	Answer	Don't know
Science and Technology	How much did they know about the body and the world around?		
War	How did war affect treatment and discovery?		
Religion	How did religious beliefs affect medicine?		
Government	How well organized were they?	Some medical schools were organized.	
Communications	How much and what sort of contact was there?		
Chance	Did unexpected things happen?	Yes, it was by chance that Paré discovered that ointment was better for gunshot wounds than boiling oil.	

1 Look at Source 1.

  a What evidence is there in this painting that Bruegel was trying to make fun of barber surgeons?

  b Think about what you have learned so far. Do you think Bruegel's criticisms are fair? Explain your answer.

  c Source 1 may be biased. Does that mean it is useless to the historian? Explain your answer.

2 Between 400 BC and AD 1685 some things in medicine changed and some things stayed the same.

  a Give examples of two things which

    ● changed

    ● stayed the same.

  b Write down one change that shows that medicine was progressing.

  c Write down one change that shows that medicine was not progressing.

  d What part did the following play in bringing about change in medicine during this time? Give one example of each:

    ● brilliant individuals

    ● chance

    ● war?

  e What factors hindered progress in medicine during this time? Give examples to support your answer.

CHAPTER 10

MEDICINE ON THE BRINK

10.1 The old order begins to change

New discoveries in science

The interest in science continued in the 18th century. Some new discoveries were made. These included:

- the microscope (1683)
- the thermometer (1709 by Fahrenheit and 1742 by Celsius)
- gases, such as hydrogen and oxygen.

Medicine

The new discoveries in science did not change anything in medicine for some time. Even so, medicine did not stand still.

Hermann Boerhaave was a doctor who told his students to watch patients carefully and take notes (see box).

Other doctors studied breathing and digestion.

Surgery improved and operations were faster. William Cheselden could take a stone out of the bladder in one minute!

Patients were glad of such speed, as there were no effective anaesthetics at this time!

HERMANN BOERHAAVE

Hermann Boerhaave taught medicine in Holland between 1718 and 1729. He taught his students to take careful notes, to make use of new ideas in science, and to do post mortems so they could work out why someone had died. His students spread his ideas all over the world. One of them, Alexander Monro, turned Edinburgh University into a great medical centre.

JOHN HUNTER

John Hunter (1728–93) is often called the 'Father of Modern Surgery'. He started his studies by doing dissections for his famous brother, William. John became a surgeon and invented new operations such as **tracheotomy** (to clear air passages). He built up a collection of anatomical specimens [bones and organs from people and animals] for doctors to study.

Source A

◄ A drawing of William Hunter's dissecting room towards the end of the 18th century.

Respect for doctors?

Surgeons became more respected during the 18th century. The Royal College of Surgeons was founded in 1800. People came to think that sick people should be properly looked after. Rich people began to set up hospitals.

Old ideas

However, many doctors still used old fashioned ideas. They used the ideas of the four humours. They thought disease could be spread by **miasmas** (bad air).

Quackery

There were, and always had been, **quack doctors**. They sold useless pills or sugared water that they said would cure everything.

New ideas

A German doctor, Franz Mesmer (1734–1815), used hypnotism to treat patients.

Source B

► Doctors sniffing the gold tops of their walking sticks which contain a liquid they thought prevented them from catching disease.

QUESTIONS

1 a Read **New discoveries in science.**
  b Write down the three new discoveries.

2 What new discoveries did Hermann Boerhaave and John Hunter make?

The state of medicine in 1820

1 Doctors still did not know what really caused disease.

2 Doctors did not know much about chemistry.

3 Doctors only had simple microscopes. They had no complicated machines to help them.

4 Surgeons did not know about infection. They did not wash before operating on people.

5 There were no proper anaesthetics. People often died from the shock of the pain.

6 During operations people often lost a lot of blood. **Blood transfusions** did not work because no one knew about blood groups.

THE GROWTH OF INDUSTRY

First Phase – 1780–1875
- **1781** The steam engine was perfected. Steam engines powered everything from pumps in coal mines to railway engines and machines to spin cotton.
- **1840s** Railways meant that people, goods and letters travelled quicker than ever before.
- **1850–75** Britain became rich by selling goods all over the world.

Second Phase – 1875–1900
- The USA, Germany and France caught up with Britain.
- New industries grew up: motor cars, firms making chemicals, firms making electrical goods like light bulbs and cookers.
- New materials came into use, including steel, rubber and aluminium.

Third Phase – 1900 onwards
- The age of high technology. Many new machines were invented. These included machines to help doctors: kidney dialysis machines (1945) and body scanners (1970s).

10.3 The impact of the Industrial Revolution

Starting in the late-18th century many changes took place in Britain. These changes are often called the Industrial Revolution.

1 The population grew.

2 More people wanted goods. Factories were started up to produce these goods.

3 At first the new factories were powered by water. Then they were powered by steam. Much later they were powered by electricity.

4 Many more people moved to the towns to work. Towns grew, but most of the new houses were badly built. There was more disease.

5 Scientists made new discoveries. This helped to conquer disease. For example, a better microscope was invented. This helped doctors to discover germs.

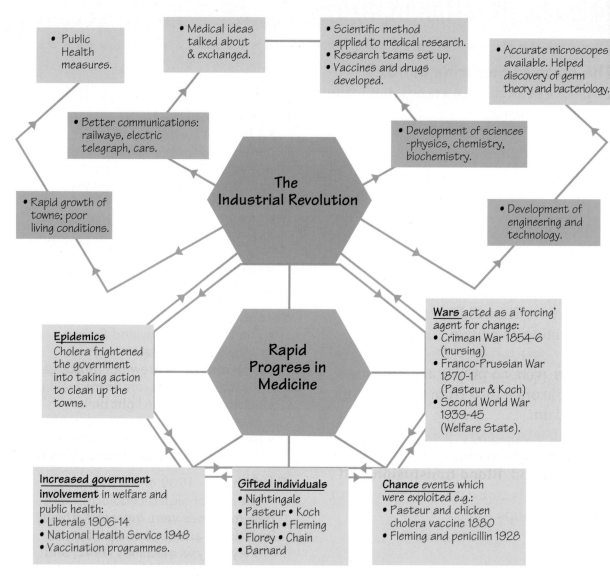

The web of factors which enabled medicine to progress very quickly after about 1850.

Within the diagram:

- Public Health measures.
- Medical ideas talked about & exchanged.
- Scientific method applied to medical research.
- Research teams set up.
- Vaccines and drugs developed.
- Accurate microscopes available. Helped discovery of germ theory and bacteriology.
- Better communications: railways, electric telegraph, cars.
- Development of sciences -physics, chemistry, biochemistry.

The Industrial Revolution

- Rapid growth of towns; poor living conditions.
- Development of engineering and technology.

Rapid Progress in Medicine

Epidemics
Cholera frightened the government into taking action to clean up the towns.

Wars acted as a 'forcing' agent for change:
- Crimean War 1854-6 (nursing)
- Franco-Prussian War 1870-1 (Pasteur & Koch)
- Second World War 1939-45 (Welfare State).

Increased government involvement in welfare and public health:
- Liberals 1906-14
- National Health Service 1948
- Vaccination programmes.

Gifted individuals
- Nightingale
- Pasteur • Koch
- Ehrlich • Fleming
- Florey • Chain
- Barnard

Chance events which were exploited e.g.:
- Pasteur and chicken cholera vaccine 1880
- Fleming and penicillin 1928

The medical revolution – 1850 to the present day

Look at the diagram above. This shows all the things that helped to make medicine progress very quickly from about 1850 to the present day. This was far faster than medicine had progressed in the 3000 years before. This rapid progress is often called the medical revolution.

QUESTIONS

1 Read **The state of medicine in 1820**. What six problems did medicine face in 1820?

2 Look at the diagram. How did epidemics help to speed up medical progress?

What did better microscopes help doctors to discover?

CHAPTER 11

THE FIGHT AGAINST INFECTIOUS DISEASE

11.1 Edward Jenner and smallpox

Smallpox was a deadly disease. It killed a lot of people. Victims got a high fever and sores full of pus all over the body. Many died. Those who survived had terrible scars and were often blind. Some people tried **inoculation** but it did not always work (see box).

Edward Jenner (1749–1823)

Jenner was a doctor from Berkeley in Gloucestershire. He had studied with John Hunter, the famous surgeon.

Jenner had heard that milkmaids who had caught the mild disease, cowpox, did not catch smallpox. He studied the milkmaids in his area. Each time there was a smallpox **epidemic**, milkmaids who had had cowpox did not catch smallpox.

In 1796 Jenner gave a healthy boy cowpox. The boy got better. Jenner then deliberately gave him a dose of smallpox (see Source A). The boy did not fall ill! Jenner called this new method **vaccination**, after the Latin word *vacca* which means 'a cow'.

Jenner could not explain how vaccination worked. So work based on it was slow to follow.

INOCULATION

An English woman, Lady Mary Wortley Montagu, learned about inoculation in Turkey. She brought the idea to England in 1718. The patient's arm was cut. A thread soaked in pus from the sores of a victim who had a mild form of smallpox was pulled through the cut. Sometimes the patient had a mild dose of smallpox, then got better. They were then safe from the deadly form of smallpox. But sometimes the inoculation gave people a heavy dose of smallpox. These people died.

Source A

I chose James Phipps, a healthy boy about eight years old. The cowpox matter was put into his arm on 14 May 1796. A week later he was a little unwell but was soon fit. Then he was inoculated with smallpox but no disease followed.

▲ Adapted from the writings of Edward Jenner, 1798.

What other doctors thought

Many doctors did not support vaccination. Some of these doctors had been inoculating people for years and had made a lot of money.

Support for vaccination

However, lots of people supported vaccination. In other countries vaccination quickly became popular. Then in Britain some members of the royal family were vaccinated. This made it popular. Parliament even gave money to Jenner for his work. By 1853, vaccination was compulsory. This was surprising, because the government usually did not make laws about what people should do for the good of their health. Smallpox slowly began to disappear.

27 October 1793 – John Moore Paget was inoculated with smallpox.

26 January 1834 – Baby Margaret was vaccinated by Mr Drake.

25 June 1844 – Jane did not go out because Richard was not well, but leeches and warm baths helped him.

▲ From the diaries of the Paget family.

▼ A cartoon drawn by James Gillray in 1802 showing that some people were afraid of what vaccination would do.

Source **C**

Source D

In 1799 John Ring met Edward Jenner. Then in 1808 Ring went to Ringwood in Hampshire to investigate some vaccination cases that were supposed to have failed. Feelings ran so high that he and his group had to carry pistols. When the British Vaccine Establishment was opened in 1809, Ring was the main vaccinator.

▲ From *The History of Wincanton* by George Sweetman, 1903.

Source E

After being vaccinated with cowpox she was very ill. Many years later she caught smallpox.

▲ C. Cooke, an apothecary, writing about a case in 1799.

Source F

In this publication it is noticed that there was a Parliamentary grant of £30,000 given to Dr Jenner for an unsuccessful experiment.

There is also a letter about the new and fatal disease, 'vaccine ulcer'. There is a letter from Ringwood proving the failures of vaccination and a list of those who died of cowpox there.

▲ Public opposition to Jenner and smallpox vaccination in the press.

Source G

Medicine has never before made such a useful improvement. In the future, people will only know about smallpox through learning history.

▲ A letter to Jenner from the President of the USA, 1802.

SUMMARY

▶ Smallpox was a deadly epidemic disease in the 18th century.

▶ A English woman brought inoculation to Britain. But it was risky and did not stop many deaths from smallpox.

▶ Jenner saw that cowpox victims did not catch smallpox.

▶ Jenner vaccinated people with cowpox.

▶ Vaccination worked. So more and more people used it.

▶ Jenner could not explain how vaccination worked. So his work did not lead on to other discoveries.

QUESTIONS

1 Look at Source B.
  a What **change** in medical practice does it show?
  b What **continuity** in medical practice does it show?

2 Look at Source C and read the caption.
  a Write a sentence describing what is happening in the cartoon.
  b What does Source C tell a historian?

3 Was Jenner's discovery of vaccination against smallpox a change or a development?

11.2 Pasteur and the germ theory

Microscopes

Microscopes meant that scientists could see micro-organisms (germs). Could this get them nearer knowing what caused disease?

Ideas about disease in 1800

Some people believed in spontaneous generation. This theory said that germs were made by disease. They did not cause it. Some of these people believed that disease was caused by gases in the air called miasmas. Others had different ideas.

Pasteur and germs

Louis Pasteur was the scientist who made the first link between germs and disease. He was not looking for this link. He made his discoveries while trying to solve problems for various manufacturing businesses.

Germs and decay

First, Pasteur showed that germs caused things to decay (go bad). He did this when he was asked to find out what made alcohol go bad while it was fermenting. He heated water in a swan-neck flask. This drove the air around the bend in the neck. The air could not get back. But when the neck of the flask was broken the air and germs got in. Decay set in. So the germs must be in the air and cause decay.

Source H

I boil some liqiud in a long-necked flask. I let it cool. In a few days little animals will grow in it. But by boiling it I had killed the germs. If I repeat the experiment but draw the neck into a curve, but still open, the liquid will remain pure for three or four years. They both contain the same liquid and they both contain air. But the difference is that in one the dust in the air and its germs can fall in, in the other they cannot.

▲ Pasteur's description of the experiment he carried out in public at the University of Paris on 7 April 1864.

Louis Pasteur was a French chemist. He was the first person to make the connection between germs and disease.

In 1857 he investigated the problem of alcohol going bad and linked germs to decay.

In 1865 he began to investigate silkworm disease. His work was interrupted by the deaths of his father and two daughters.

In 1868 he had a brain haemorrhage and was paralysed on one side. By 1877 he was back at work.

Pasteur's achievements

- discovered that heating liquid kills germs. This is called 'pasteurization'.
- developed a vaccine for chicken cholera (1880).
- developed a vaccine for anthrax (1881).
- developed a vaccine for rabies (1885).

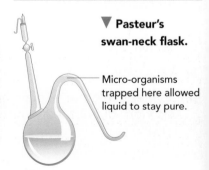

▼ Pasteur's swan-neck flask.

Micro-organisms trapped here allowed liquid to stay pure.

▲ This print of Pasteur working in his laboratory was made when Pasteur was famous.

ROBERT KOCH
(1843–1910)

Robert Koch was a German doctor who first showed that a particular germ caused a particular disease.

Using the new discoveries in chemical dyes and photography, Koch could colour germs so they showed up clearly. He then photographed them.

In 1882 he discovered the germ that caused tuberculosis.

In 1883 he discovered the germ that caused cholera.

Koch won the Nobel Prize in 1905 for his work.

11.3 Robert Koch

Pasteur proved that germs cause disease. He could not prove which germ caused which disease. It was a German doctor, Robert Koch, who did this.

Koch and anthrax
In 1872 Koch began to study **anthrax**, an animal disease that could spread to humans. He studied the blood of animals with and without the disease. By 1875 he had found the germ.

Koch and blood poisoning
Koch then studied the germ that caused blood poisoning. The germ was so small that he could not see it. How could he study it? How could he show it caused disease?

New technology
Koch used new chemical dyes to stain the germ so it could be seen. He then used a new kind of photographic lens to record how, under the microscope, the germ bred until it was the only germ in the blood. If it was the only germ then it must be the cause of the disease.

▼ Robert Koch is shown as St George defeating tuberculosis.

Germ hunters

Soon everyone was looking for germs. Once the germs were discovered, vaccines and drugs could be made.

Year	Germ discovered	Name of scientist
1879	Leprosy	Hansen
1880	Typhoid	Eberth
1882	Diphtheria	Klebs
1884	Tetanus	Nicholaier
1884	Pneumonia	Frankael
1894	Plague	Kitasato and Yersin

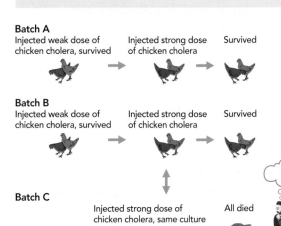

Batch A
Injected weak dose of chicken cholera, survived   Injected strong dose of chicken cholera   Survived

Batch B
Injected weak dose of chicken cholera, survived   Injected strong dose of chicken cholera   Survived

Batch C
Injected strong dose of chicken cholera, same culture   All died

▲ How Pasteur discovered the principle of making vaccines from the germs of the disease chicken cholera.

11.4 Vaccines

Chicken cholera vaccine

Pasteur read about what Koch had discovered. He wanted to make more discoveries for France, because France had been beaten by Germany in the Franco-Prussian War of 1870–1. Pasteur built up a team of scientists to work with him. He was asked to look into the disease of chicken cholera.

Pasteur took some blood from sick chickens and grew the germs in a broth. His assistant, Charles Chamberland, was in charge of injecting the germ broth into the chickens. He went on holiday and left the broth in the flask, open to the air. When he got back he injected the chickens with the germ broth. The chickens did not die.

Chamberland told Pasteur what had happened. They made a new germ broth and injected the chickens again. But still they did not die (see Batch A above). They tried the whole thing all over again with a new batch of chickens. The chickens still did not die (Batch B). Finally, they injected another batch of chickens with a fresh broth of strong germs only. All of them died (Batch C).

Pasteur realized that leaving the broth uncovered had weakened the germs. The weak germs had helped the chickens in Batches A and B to fight off the stronger, deadly germs. This way of making a vaccine is called attenuation.

Pasteur and anthrax

Pasteur wanted to find a vaccine for the deadly disease of anthrax. Dr. Emile Roux worked with Pasteur. Roux made a weak anthrax germ. Then came the test.

Testing the vaccine

In 1881 Pasteur was asked to prove that his new anthrax vaccine worked. He went to a farm near Paris. There were 60 sheep:

- 25 were injected with the weak anthrax germ (vaccine). Then later with a deadly dose of strong anthrax.
- 25 were injected with a deadly dose of strong anthrax.
- 10 were left alone.

Result

Within a month only the sheep that had been vaccinated were alive and well.

News of Pasteur's success was reported all over the world. Soon many animals were vaccinated against anthrax.

The death rate from anthrax in animals went down quickly. Farmers were saved a lot of money.

This research helped human medicine too. It made people happier about vaccination. If it worked on animals it would also work on humans.

Source K

Will you have some microbe? There is some everywhere. The learned Monsieur Pasteur, has spoken. The microbe alone is the characteristic of a disease.

▲ From an article in the *Veterinary Press* which made fun of the germ theory.

Source L

Paris 2 June 9.30pm [by telegraph from our correspondents]
Today I went to see the result of an experiment by M. Pasteur.

On 5 May, 25 sheep were marked with a hole in their ear and injected with anthrax vaccine.

On 31 May all 50 sheep were injected with the anthrax vaccine.

By 2 June, 23 of the unvaccinated sheep were dead. Two more died an hour later. The sheep which had been vaccinated frolicked and stayed healthy.

▲ A report from *The Times*, Friday 3 June 1881.

QUESTIONS

1 Read **Robert Koch** on page 85.

   What new discoveries did he use so that he could see germs more clearly?

Rabies

Rabies is a deadly disease. Pasteur wanted to make a rabies vaccine. His assistant, Emile Roux, kept the spines of dead rabbits who had died of rabies. He kept testing to see how long the rabies germ stayed alive in the dead spine.

Pasteur sees Roux's work

Pasteur copied Roux's idea. Roux was angry. Pasteur began to test a vaccine from the rabbit's spines on dogs. He injected a dog with weak germs from a 14 day-old rabbit spine. Then a 13 day-old spine and so on. The last injection contained very strong germs from the spine of a freshly dead rabbit. The dogs he treated like this did not get rabies.

The boy who was dying of rabies

Pasteur was not sure if the rabies vaccine would work on humans. Then one day in 1885, Joseph Meister arrived at Pasteur's laboratory. He was covered with bites from a rabid dog. He was going to die anyway. Pasteur decided to try injecting the vaccine. It worked. Soon Pasteur vaccinated lots of people against rabies.

Diphtheria

The germ of diphtheria was discovered by Edwin Klebs, a German doctor. But he could not find out how to stop the disease. Many scientists, including Emile Roux and Emil von Behring (a student of Robert Koch), worked to find an injection to prevent the disease.

Tuberculosis

Koch was working on a vaccine for **tuberculosis** (TB). The German government pressed him to show how good it was at an International Medical Congress in 1890. Lots of people with tuberculosis flocked to see Koch but the vaccine did not work. Koch was blamed but work on finding new vaccines went on.

Governments

The French government knew that the work of Pasteur made France famous. The German government felt the same way about Koch. Both men were given money and buildings where they could carry on their research.

▲ Removing saliva from a rabid dog.

Source **N**

Joseph Meister, aged nine years, was knocked over and bitten by a rabid dog.

Some bites were so deep as to make walking difficult. The dog was certainly rabid.

The death of this child being certain, I decided to try the method which had been successful with dogs.

Meister was injected with liquid from the spine of a rabbit which had died of rabies fifteen days before.

He survived.

▲ Pasteur's description of the rabies injection.

Factors which enabled Pasteur and Koch to succeed

Industry, science & technology
- The much improved microscope allowed bacteria to be studied.
- Koch used industrial chemical dyes to stain bacteria.

Communications
- The results of experiments and research were spread quickly via telegraph, newspapers and journals. Railways enabled scientists to meet regularly.

Research techniques
- Both Pasteur and Koch devised experiments to prove theories.
- Both had research teams.

Factors which enabled Pasteur and Koch to succeed

Personal qualities
- Both men were intelligent, persistent and determined.
- Both spoke in public at the risk of abuse from doubters.

Chance events
- Chamberland's 'mistake' when Pasteur was researching a vaccine for chicken cholera.
- The surprise arrival of Joseph Meister allowed Pasteur to test his rabies vaccine on humans.

War
- The Franco-Prussian War (1870–1) ended in a disastrous defeat for the French. Tension between the two countries followed.
- Pasteur and Koch were spurred on by this tension. They became rivals; a new discovery brought prestige for their country.

QUESTIONS

1 Look at the **SUMMARY**.

   a Did anyone know what caused disease in 1850?

   b What did Pasteur discover in 1857?

   c What did Pasteur prove in 1864?

   d What new inventions helped scientists to learn from other scientists?

2 Pasteur and Koch discovered that germs cause disease. Because their countries were rivals, so were they. Write a sentence or two to explain if this helped the progress of medicine, or held it back.

3 Look at Source J on page 85 and Source M on page 88. Why do you think such pictures were made?

SUMMARY

▶ **1850** No one knew what caused disease.

▶ **1857** Pasteur discovered that something in the air caused sugar beet juice to go bad.

▶ **1864** Pasteur proved his germ theory [that germs are in the air] in a public experiment in Paris.

▶ Robert Koch started to study anthrax. He proved that one sort of germ caused one sort of disease.

▶ Pasteur and Koch built up teams of scientists to help them to make more discoveries.

▶ All the scientists learned from each other. The electric telegraph, railways and newspapers meant that scientists learnt what other scientists were doing.

An infectious disease is a disease you can catch from someone else. This includes colds, 'flu, chicken-pox and measles. In the past it included diphtheria, smallpox and cholera.

Keeping clean

Germs grow best in dirt. So governments passed laws to make sure sewage was taken away from houses and that clean water was piped into houses.

Vaccines

By 1900 scientists, like Pasteur, had discovered germs. They had made vaccines to prevent people and animals catching terrible diseases such as rabies and anthrax. They knew what caused infectious diseases and how to prevent healthy people from getting them.

But no one knew how to kill off the germs in a person who already had the disease (without killing the person as well).

Paul Ehrlich and the magic bullet

Paul Ehrlich first worked on diphtheria. He was fascinated to see the way that the body made **antibodies**.

These antibodies could attack and destroy germs in a person's body. The antibodies homed in on the germs like a magic bullet. Sometimes the antibodies did not succeed. They needed help.

Ehrlich wanted to find a chemical that homed in on a certain germ and killed that germ inside the sick person.

PAUL EHRLICH

Ehrlich was born in Germany in 1854.

He studied chemistry and bacteriology [the study of germs]. He worked as a doctor.

In 1889, after he had recovered from tuberculosis (TB), he joined Koch's team at the Institute for Infectious Diseases in Berlin.

He helped Behring in his research on diphtheria.

From 1899 he studied the treatment of disease with chemicals.

He shared the Nobel Prize for medicine in 1908.

He died in 1915.

◀ **Factors involved in the discovery of Salvarsan 606.**

The search for a chemical to destroy syphilis

Syphilis was a sexually transmitted disease that killed thousands of people every year. Ehrlich and his team made up and tested over 600 mixtures of arsenic. They hoped that one of them might kill the syphilis germ. All of them seemed to be useless.

Sahachiro Hata

Hata was Japanese. He joined Ehrlich's team in 1909. He was asked to re-test the arsenic mixtures that had been tested and rejected. To his surprise he found that mixture number 606 worked. It did kill the syphilis germ. Perhaps someone made a mistake before.

Salvarsan 606

Ehrlich called the new medicine, Salvarsan 606. He found it worked on rabbits with syphilis without killing the rabbits. Because it had arsenic (a poison) in it, he insisted on tests on hundreds of rabbits before it was tried on people. In 1911 it was tried on a human being. It worked.

Doctors against Salvarsan 606

Some doctors said Salvarsan 606 was too painful to inject. Some doctors were worried about injecting patients with arsenic, despite all Ehrlich's tests. Some doctors said that people would have sex with lots of different people now they knew that syphilis could be cured.

QUESTIONS

1 Read **Keeping clean**. What did governments do to help people keep clean?

2 Read **Sahachiro Hata**.

   a Who discovered Salvarsan 606?

   b 'Salvarsan 606 was discovered by chance'. Do you agree with this statement? Write a sentence explaining your reasons.

2 Why were some doctors against Salvarsan 606?

3 List some other ideas in medicine that were not accepted at first.

Sulphonamide drugs

Gerhard Domagk, another German scientist, admired Ehrlich's work. He wanted to find more magic bullets that would kill germs but not the sick person.

Germanin and prontosil

Domagk discovered germanin, a drug which worked against sleeping sickness. Then, in 1932, he discovered prontosil. This was made from a red dye and it killed the germ that caused blood poisoning. It worked on mice but he did not know if it would work on humans.

Then, in 1935, his daughter was injured by an infected needle. The wound turned bad and she was very ill with blood poisoning. Domagk gave her prontosil and she recovered.

What was in the prontosil?

Other scientists discovered that the important part of prontosil was sulphonamide made from coal tar.

Soon they made other medicines from sulphonamides. These medicines helped against diseases like scarlet fever, tonsillitis and pneumonia

Disadvantages of sulphonamides

Sulphonamides could damage a person's kidneys and liver. Also, they did not work against very strong germs. An even better magic bullet was needed.

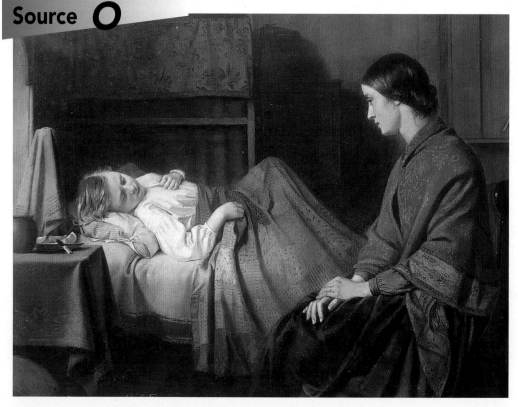

Source O

◀ A painting from the 1860s called *An Anxious Hour*. Before sulphonamide drugs, many children died of common illnesses such as 'flu.

The story of penicillin

Penicillin was the first **antibiotic**. It was the first drug made from living things like fungi. It stopped bacteria (germs) growing. Three people worked to discover it: Alexander Fleming, Howard Florey and Ernst Chain.

Alexander Fleming: the man who didn't invent penicillin

If you ask people what Alexander Fleming did they will probably tell you that he was the first person to discover penicillin. This is not true.

What is penicillin?

When cheese or fruit goes bad, mould grows on it. This mould has a Latin name *penicillium*. It has become known as penicillin.

Source P

In 1881, a nurse was injured in a road accident. Her wound became infected. Antiseptics did not stop the infection. Then a different treatment was tried. It was so successful that she wrote down the name. It was 'penicillium'.

▲ Adapted from a book about Fleming published in 1985.

Joseph Lister and penicillin

In 1871 Joseph Lister began experimenting with penicillium. Source P shows the new treatment was successful.

For some unknown reason Lister did not continue his studies on penicillium. Other scientists also worked on penicillium but no one could make it in large amounts. There was not enough to treat patients.

ALEXANDER FLEMING
(1881–1955)

Career: Qualified as a doctor in 1906.

Worked as a research assistant for Sir Almroth Wright, head of the Inoculation Department at St. Mary's Hospital, London.

Worked in an army hospital in France in the First World War.

Returned to St. Mary's Hospital after the war to work in research.

Honours: knighted in 1944 (became Sir Alexander Fleming).

Won Nobel Prize for Medicine in 1945 (with Florey and Chain).

Fleming's discovery

During the First World War Fleming worked in an army hospital in France. He was appalled to see that antiseptics did not work on deep wounds. After the war, Fleming returned to St. Mary's Hospital in London. He wanted to find something that would kill germs more successfully.

A chance discovery

By 1928, Fleming was studying staphylococci (germs which make wounds go bad). He grew the germs in little dishes.

One day he was cleaning out a dish when he noticed that some mould was growing in it. This often happened. But this time Fleming noticed that all around the mould, the germs had stopped growing!

Was the mould killing the germs?

Fleming grew more of the mould (*penecilium notatum*). He made a juice from the mould and called it penicillin, after the mould itself. This penicillin juice killed many deadly germs if he injected it into sick animals. The animals got better.

But no one was interested enough to give Fleming any money to make a pure drug for human beings.

In 1929 Fleming wrote an article about penicillin. He then stopped working on it. Nothing more happened for six years.

Source Q

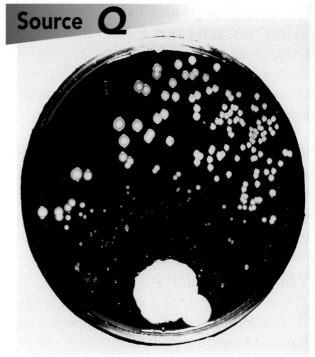

▲ The dish with the 'abnormal' culture. The mould is at the bottom. At the top, germs are growing but near the mould there is a clear area.

Source R

I saw bacteria fading away around the mould. I did not know I had got the clue to the most powerful substance yet that would defeat bacterial infection.

▲ Adapted from a speech by Fleming in 1943.

QUESTIONS

Read **A chance discovery**.

1 a What germs was Fleming studying in 1928?

   b What did these germs do?

2 What stopped Fleming doing more work on penicillin?

Howard Florey and Ernst Chain

In 1935 Howard Florey headed a team of brilliant scientists at Oxford.

One of these scientists was Ernst Chain, a Jewish refugee from Nazi Germany. Chain read the old article written by Fleming about penicillin.

Florey and Chain decided to try and make penicillin themselves. They managed to do this and tested it on sick mice. The mice got better. Florey said it was a miracle.

Not too optimistic

However, Florey did not want to get too excited. He explained later on that it might not work for human beings. 'A man is 3000 times as big as a mouse', he said.

Problems of making pure penicillin

Florey and Chain grew the mould in milk bottles and bed pans. They had no money to make penicillin on a big scale.

By 1940 they had made enough to treat a policeman who was dying from blood poisoning. He got much better. Then the penicillin ran out and he died. But Florey and Chain had proved it worked.

The Second World War

During the Second World War Britain was fighting Germany. All the big chemical factories were making bombs and did not have time to try and make penicillin. So Florey went to the USA. Still no one would give him the money to make large amounts of penicillin.
Then, in 1941, the USA joined the war against Germany. The US government gave money to chemical firms so they could buy equipment to make penicillin on a huge scale.

The D-Day invasion

When the Allies launched the D-day invasion of Europe there was enough penicillin to treat all the wounded soldiers. Thousands of lives were saved.

Source S

I don't think it ever entered our minds about suffering humanity. This was an interesting scientific exercise.

▲ A comment made by Howard Florey in an interview in 1957.

QUESTIONS

Read **Not too optimistic**.

1 Why was Florey not too optimistic about his success with the mice?

Factors in the development of penicillin

The penicillin story shows how a number of factors worked together to bring about an important discovery. These factors were:

- chance
- governments
- war
- research teams
- individual brilliance.

Chance (or luck)

This is the factor usually associated with Fleming's discovery. Certainly Fleming only found the mould by chance. But was it really chance? If Fleming had been a less observant person he might not have noticed what the mould was doing. So you could say it was the result of individual brilliance, not chance. However Fleming did not take the discovery further.

War and governments

Many soldiers were dying of infected wounds during the war. The British and US governments put large sums of money into mass producing penicillin. However, neither Fleming nor Florey and Chain did the work on penicillin just because of the Second World War. So it is not so straightforward as that.

Research teams and individual brilliance

Florey and Chain led a team of researchers. The work of all these researchers helped to develop penicillin. Florey and Chain also said that they probably would have done the research even if they had not read about Fleming's discovery. It would just have taken longer.

Fleming's dying friend

In 1942, Alexander Fleming's friend was dying. Fleming asked Florey if he could have some penicillin. Florey sent some and the friend got better. The story appeared in *The Times* newspaper. This was followed by a letter from Sir Almroth Wright (see Source U).

Stage 1 1928

Alexander Fleming discovered the penicillin mould. He was unable to produce pure penicillin from the mould. He published a report of his work but did no more.

Stage 2 1938–41

A team of researchers at Oxford University, led by Howard Florey and Ernst Chain, developed a method of making pure penicillin. They could not make large amounts however.

Stage 3 1941–44

In 1941 the USA entered the Second World War. The US government funded research into methods of making large quantities of penicillin. By 1944 enough penicillin was available for Allied soldiers.

Stages in the penicillin story. ▶

The Fleming 'myth'

Suddenly everyone began to say that Fleming alone had discovered penicillin.

The Nobel Prize

Florey, Chain and Fleming were given the Nobel Prize together in 1945. But it is Fleming who has become famous for discovering penicillin.

Source U

Professor Alexander Fleming of this laboratory is the discoverer of penicillin and also the author of the original suggestion that it might ... have important uses in medicine.

▲ From a letter written to *The Times* by Sir Almroth Wright, 20 August 1942.

Source V

There had been a lot in the newspapers and press about penicillin. It is presented as worked out by Fleming. Some scientists have now said to us, 'But I thought you had done something on penicillin too'.

▲ Extract from a letter written by Howard Florey to Sir Henry Dale in December 1942. Dale was the president of the Royal Society, a body concerned with the advancement of science and medicine.

Source T

▲ A stained glass window, showing Alexander Fleming at work in his laboratory. It is in a church close to the hospital where Fleming worked for 49 years.

QUESTIONS

1 Read **The Fleming 'myth'** and Source U.

   a What is the Fleming 'myth'?

   b Who started the Fleming 'myth'?

2 If you knew that for many years before 1900 mould had been used by people in different parts of the world to treat wounds would you say that the work of Fleming, Florey and Chain was not a breakthrough in the history of medicine? Explain your answer.

Antibiotics

The Second World War ended in 1945. Penicillin was available for everyone. The first antibiotics had been born.

Different antibiotics

The drug companies know that if they find drugs that are able to cure or prevent illness they will make huge profits. There are now hundreds of antibiotics being made. For example streptomycin was discovered in 1944. It is very effective against tuberculosis.

Allergies

People who are allergic to penicillin can be given one of many other antibiotics.

Why has illness not ended?

Drug companies have developed more and more drugs. But sometimes the drugs turn out to be less effective than we would like.

Thalidomide

In the early 1960s a new drug was developed. It was called thalidomide. It was given to women who were suffering from morning sickness during pregnancy. The drug worked. However, it caused harm to the unborn child. As a result of the mothers taking thalidomide a number of children were born with severely deformed limbs. Later it was discovered that the effects of thalidomide were passed on from generation to generation. The drug companies had to pay compensation.

Committee on Safety of Drugs

In 1964, the government set up the Committee on Safety of Drugs. Its job was to check all developed drugs.

Source W

£485,000 DAMAGES FOR 28 THALIDOMIDE CHILDREN

Agreed damages totalling £485,528 were awarded in the High Court yesterday to 28 deformed children who were affected by the drug thalidomide.

Seeking approval for the settlements, Mr Desmond Ackner, the children's lawyer, revealed that negotiations were taking place to provide for 300 other children thought to have been deformed by thalidomide.

Discussions were being held with the Distillers Company (Biochemicals) Ltd. to set up a trust. This would save the 'years of time' it would take to deal with all the children on an individual basis.

▲ An article from the *Daily Telegraph*, July 1970.

Busy people and antibiotics

Busy people often demand antibiotics so they can be cured instantly. This means that antibiotics have been overused.

Problems with overuse of antibiotics

Bacteria (germs that can cause infection) can form defences against antibiotics. They do this by mutating new forms of bacteria.

The antibiotics do not kill the new forms of bacteria. Scientists then have to discover new antibiotics.

Superbugs

Scientists call bacteria which are resistant to antibiotics 'superbugs'.

AIDS

AIDS stands for Acquired Immune Deficiency Syndrome. It is a new disease. No cure has yet been found. It was first noticed in 1981. US doctors found that large numbers of gay young men were dying. By 1983 the HIV virus had been discovered to be the cause. No one is sure where the disease comes from. By the end of 2001, it had killed almost 25 million people.

	Adults (millions)	Children under 15 (millions)
No. of people living with AIDS	37.2	2.7
AIDS deaths up to 2001	17.5	4.3
AIDS deaths in 2001	2.4	0.6
No. of children orphaned by AIDS		13.2 million

The proportion of adults living with AIDS in 2001	
Africa, south of the Sahara	8.4%
Caribbean	2.2%
North America	0.6%
South and South East Asia	0.6%
South America	0.5%
Western Europe	0.3%

Tuberculosis

Doctors thought that they had conquered tuberculosis. However, it is showing signs of being resistant to antibiotics. The illness is now increasing worldwide.

Genetic engineering – hope for the future?

Scientists are now able to study the body's cells and the genes and chromosomes within the cells.

Now that scientists can study the genes, they can also treat them. This is called genetic engineering. The scientists can alter the genetic material by destroying specific damaged or diseased cells. This can help to treat some illnesses, such as certain sorts of cancer.

Some scientists believe that it will be possible to **clone** spare body parts. These body parts can then be used to replace damaged or diseased parts of our bodies.

QUESTIONS

1 What lessons can we learn about medicine from:
a the Thalidomide affair
b superbugs
c AIDS?

SUMMARY

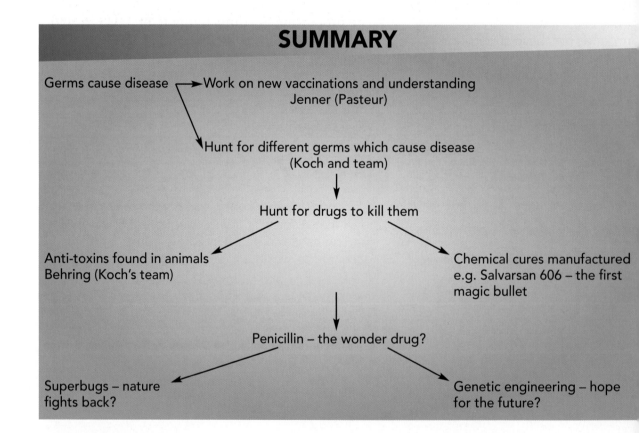

Germs cause disease →Work on new vaccinations and understanding Jenner (Pasteur)

Hunt for different germs which cause disease (Koch and team)

Hunt for drugs to kill them

Anti-toxins found in animals Behring (Koch's team)

Chemical cures manufactured e.g. Salvarsan 606 – the first magic bullet

Penicillin – the wonder drug?

Superbugs – nature fights back?

Genetic engineering – hope for the future?

Source 1

▲ Pasteur and his team. Dr Emile Roux, his main assistant, is seated on his right. Albert Calmette who, together with Camille Guerin, discovered a vaccine against TB in 1906, is seated on the far right of Pasteur.

Source 2

Pasteur was a small man who inspired devotion. He had aggressive manners and always wanted to show he was more clever than anyone else.

He loved France and hated Prussia (part of Germany). There was a war between France and Prussia in 1870.

Pasteur also wanted to be famous.

▲ Adapted from *Microbes and Men* by Robert Reid, 1974.

Source 3

Koch said that Pasteur had not done anything new in science. Pasteur lost his temper and years of hatred came out. Yet Pasteur had been full of great ideas. But Koch had the scientific skill to make things work.

▲ Adapted from *Microbes and Men* by Robert Reid, 1974.

Source 4

You must keep a careful check on the rabid dogs and a daily written record of what happens to them, making it clear if they become ill or not, or if they are cured.

▲ From a letter written by Louis Pasteur to his assistant in his research on the rabies vaccine.

Source 5

▲ Louis Pasteur vaccinating a sheep against anthrax in 1881.

1 Look at Sources 1–4.
   What factors enabled Pasteur to make his discoveries? Choose the ones that you think are important from the list below:

- he was a small man
- he inspired devotion
- he loved France
- he wanted to be famous
- he was very aggressive
- he wanted everyone to think he was clever
- he was full of great ideas
- he hated Koch
- he had a bad temper
- he was very thorough in checking his experiments
- he trained his assistants to be thorough.

2 Look at Source 2.
   Does this picture support any of the factors in the list above? Explain your answer.

3 Three of the many people who were working in medicine in the 19th century were:

- Pasteur
- Ehrlich
- Koch.

Which of these three do you think made the most important contribution? Explain your answer.

CHAPTER 12

THE REVOLUTION IN SURGERY

12.1 Anaesthetics conquer pain

The problems of surgery
Surgeons had always faced three main problems: pain, infection and bleeding.

The problem of pain
For hundreds of years there were no good pain-killers. Surgeons cut off arms and legs or took out stones and the patient screamed with pain. Often they died from the shock of the pain.

Chemist discovers laughing gas
Humphrey Davy was a chemist. In 1799 he discovered people did not feel pain if they breathed in nitrous oxide (laughing gas). He wrote about his discovery but surgeons ignored it.

Anaesthetics are pain-killing drugs. There are two sorts:

General anaesthetics – These make the patient completely unconscious.

Local anaesthetics – These stop pain in one place, such as in a tooth.

Source A

Source B

A patient getting ready for an operation was like a prisoner condemmed to death.

▲ Said in 1848, by someone who had surgery before effective anaesthetics.

◀ A cartoon of an operation in 1793.

The search for a good anaesthetic
In 1842 Crawford Long used ether as a general anaesthetic. It worked but he did not tell anyone about it.

Nitrous oxide
Horace Wells was an American dentist. In 1845 he went to a fair and saw people breathing in nitrous oxide for fun. They laughed a lot. They also felt no pain at all. The next day Wells had a tooth out. He breathed nitrous oxide first. He felt no pain at all. But Wells did not know that some people are not affected by nitrous oxide. When he tried to show a group of students how to take a tooth out without pain, the patient shouted with pain.

Problems with nitrous oxide
Wells used nitrous oxide in several more operations where it worked. Then a patient died from being given too much. Wells killed himself. William Morton, Wells' partner, looked for a safer anaesthetic.

A safer anaesthetic – ether
Morton found that ether worked well. In 1846 he and John Warren cut a tumour off Gilbert Abbott's neck. They gave him ether first. He did not feel a thing.

Spreading the news
This time news spread fast. A doctor who had seen the operation on Abbot wrote an article about it the next week. He also wrote a letter to a friend in Britain. The letter went by the fast steamship that now crossed the Atlantic. By 19 December 1846 the friend, Dr Boot, had the letter and had taken a tooth out using ether. On 21 December Robert Liston amputated a man's leg using ether.

Source C

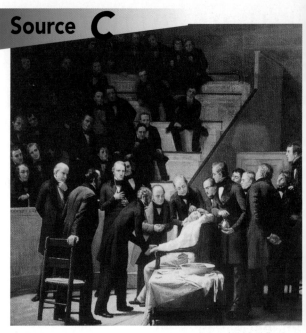

▲ Warren's operation on Gilbert Abbott, painted in 1882.

Source D

This Yankee dodge, gentlemen, beats mesmerism hollow!

▲ Said by Robert Liston to the people who had watched him operate in 1846.

QUESTIONS

1 Draw out a chart like the one below. Fill in the chart to show when experiments were made with anaesthetics.

Date	Event	Person(s) involved

2 Source C was painted long after the operation. Is it a reliable source of evidence for a historian? Give reasons for your answer.

Problems with ether

Ether could catch fire. It had a strong smell and made patients cough a lot.

James Young Simpson and chloroform

Simpson wanted to find a better anaesthetic than ether. He particularly wanted to help women with pain in childbirth. In 1847 he discovered that chloroform was easier to breathe in. Not very much was needed and it knocked people out quickly (see Source E).

Some people were against anaesthetics

- Some people thought doctors did not know how much to give or what side effects there might be. (Some patients did die of anaesthetics).

- Members of the Calvinist Church in Scotland said that the Bible said women were supposed to suffer pain in childbirth.

- Some people worried that surgeons could cut off whatever they liked while the patient was unconscious!

- Some army doctors thought using anaesthetics was 'soft'.

- There had been cases of ether exploding in the operating theatre.

Source E

Late one evening Dr. Simpson and his two friends sat down [to try out different anaesthetics].

Having sniffed several substances, Dr. Simpson decided to try one that he did not think was much use – a small bottle of chloroform. He found it under a pile of paper. [They breathed in the chloroform and passed out].

When he woke up Dr. Simpson thought, 'This is far stronger and better than ether.'

▲ From H. L. Gordon, *Sir James Young Simpson and Chloroform*, 1897.

Source F

▲ A drawing showing the effect on Simpson and his friends of breathing in chloroform.

Queen Victoria and chloroform

Queen Victoria had chloroform for the birth of her eighth child in 1853. The Queen wrote that chloroform 'was soothing, quietening and delightful.' After this lots of people began to think it was a good idea. It was used a lot until 1900. Then it was discovered it could damage the liver. Surgeons went back to using ether.

Problems with anaesthetics

Anaesthetics were wonderful. For the first time in history patients could have operations without pain. But there were problems. Sometimes so much anaesthetic had to be used (to relax the muscles) that patients slept for days.

New anaesthetics

In 1884 cocaine was used as a local anaesthetic. Then, in 1905, novocaine was found to work better. In 1942 curare, a South American poison, was used to relax muscles and worked very well.

Anaesthetists today

Anaesthetists are specially skilled doctors. They give the anaesthetic. They monitor the heart beat, blood pressure, breathing and brain waves on high technology machines.

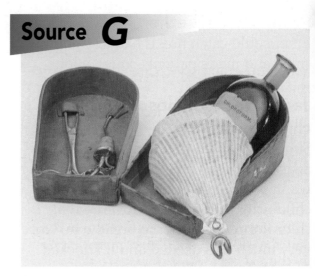

▲ An inhaler for breathing in chloroform from 1879.

QUESTIONS

1 Write down the three problems with ether.

2 Write a short paragraph saying who was against anaesthetics and why.

3 Why did more people start to use chloroform after 1853?

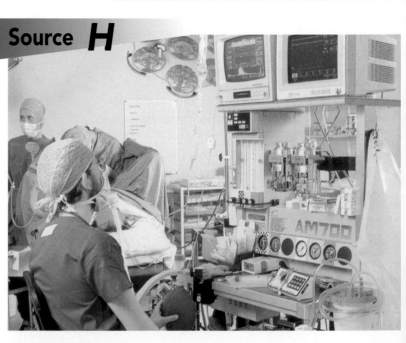

Source **H**

▶ Modern anaesthetists at work.

12.2 The problem of infection

The problem of infection
From 1846 there were anaesthetics. So surgeons did a lot more operations. But still many patients died. The time from 1846–70 is sometimes called the 'black period' of surgery. Surgeons wore old blood-stained clothes. They did not wash their hands or their knives. The trouble was surgeons did not know about germs.

Ignaz Semmelweiss and puerperal fever
Semmelweiss was a doctor in Vienna in the 1840s. He was worried that so many women died after childbirth from puerperal fever. They had the baby. They seemed to be weak but all right. Then they got a fever and died. In 1847 Semmelweiss said that he thought the fever was spread by the doctors themselves. Doctors dissected women who had died of puerperal fever. Then they went straight from the dissecting room to examine women who had just had a baby. They did not even wash their hands.

Semmelweiss ordered that all doctors working for him washed their hands in a solution of chloride of lime before they examined their patients. After this fewer women died but other doctors did not accept what Semmelweiss said.

Joseph Lister and antiseptics
Lister read about Pasteur's work on the germ theory. Lister realized that germs were killing his patients. He decided to kill the germs instead.

Carbolic acid
Lister used carbolic acid to kill germs. It is very strong. At first he soaked bandages in it. He found that the wounds did not go bad. But the patient was burned by the carbolic acid. Next he decided to use it as a spray. Everything in the operating theatre was sprayed with carbolic acid, including the surgeon's hands, the knives and the patient. Far fewer patients died.

JOSEPH LISTER
(1828–1912)

Lister was Professor of Surgery at Glasgow. Many doctors were against his ideas but it was soon obvious that his antiseptic carbolic acid worked.

The figures below come from his records of amputations. They show how useful antiseptics were.

Date	No. of patients	% died
1864–6 (no antiseptics)	35	46%
1867–70 (antiseptics)	40	15%

Source 1

Chance did not play a part in Lister's discovery. He had read of the germ theory and had applied it.

Millions of lives were saved by the new idea of antisepsis [the use of antiseptics to kill germs].

The frightful spectre [of death] which had haunted operating theatres had been shown to have a cause. Lister had shown how to defeat it.

▲ Adapted from *Microbes and Men* by Robert Reid, 1974.

Source J

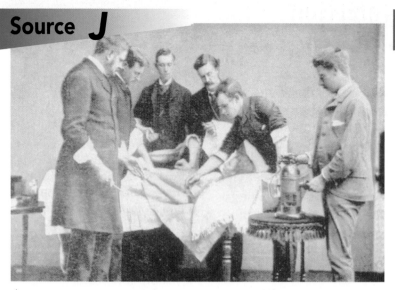

▲ An operation in the 1880s. Lister's steam carbolic spray is being used.

Source K

Lots of people were against Lister and his ideas of antiseptics such as carbolic acid killing germs.

Full 20 years were needed before British surgeons were won over to Lister's idea.

▲ Adapted from Leo M. Zimmereman and Ilza Veith, *Great Ideas in the History of Surgery*, 1961.

Aseptic surgery (keeping clean)

Antiseptics such as carbolic acid burnt the skin. So surgeons in Germany decided to keep all germs out of operating theatres if they could. Everything was washed and sterilized. For instance, all the knives were sterilized by passing superheated steam over them. This was called aseptic surgery.

Rubber gloves

William S. Halsted was a leading US surgeon. In 1889 his nurse (and future wife) complained that the antiseptic chemicals he used were ruining her hands. Halsted asked the Goodyear Rubber Company to make some rubber gloves she could wear. He quickly realised that these clean gloves kept germs away from patients. Soon he made his team of doctors and nurses wear caps, masks and gowns for surgery.

Source L

▲ Halsted in the operating theatre. He operated and taught his students at the same time.

Plastic surgery

Surgeons in India and in Europe had patched injured skin for hundreds of years, but there was a chance it might go bad.

In the 20th century two world wars and new weapons meant that many people had bad injuries. In Britain, Harold Gillies was the first plastic surgeon to work to help badly injured people look better.

In the Second World War, Gillie's assistant, Archibald McIndoe, set up a special hospital to treat patients (mostly airmen) who had been badly burned by petrol.

The use of the new drugs, sulphonamides and penicillin, helped him in his work by keeping infection down.

Source M

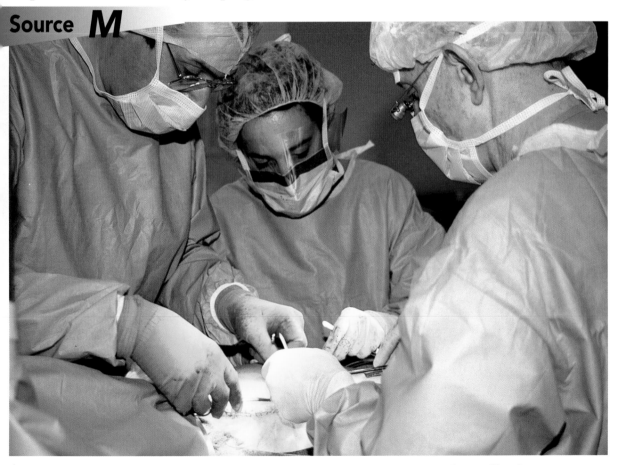

▲ A modern plastic surgery operation. The patient is undergoing reconstruction of one of her breasts following treatment for breast cancer.

ARCHIBALD MCINDOE
'The face-builder'

Born: New Zealand in 1900.

Career: Studied medicine in New Zealand and in England.

After the First World War he worked with Harold Gillies. They treated patients who had been disfigured as a result of war wounds.

During the Second World War, McIndoe ran a plastic surgery unit at East Grinstead in England. He specialised in plastic surgery on the faces and limbs of airmen who had suffered burns when their planes had been shot down.

Honours: knighted in 1947 (became Sir Archibald McIndoe)

Died 1960. Because of all his work for injured airmen, his ashes were buried in the RAF church in London.

Discoveries that have helped surgery since 1895

X-rays
In 1895 Wilhelm Rontgen discovered X-rays. Surgeons could see pictures of the inside of a person's body without cutting them open.

Radium
In 1898 Marie and Pierre Curie discovered radium. This later helped to treat cancer.

Electrocardiograph
In 1903 Willem Einthoven developed electrocardiographs. These monitored the heartbeat.

Artificial kidney machine
In 1943 a Dutch surgeon, Willem Kolf made the first artificial kidney machine.

Heart-lung machine
In 1953 a heart-lung machine was used in an operation. The patient's heart was stopped for some time. The machine took over. This gave the surgeons more time to operate.

Microsurgery
In the 1960s new microscopes, fine needles and threads meant surgeons could sew up tiny nerves and blood vessels.

Fibre optics
Today fibre optics mean that surgeons can see inside the body by putting fine tubes through the mouth or rectum, or through a keyhole sized cut.

New plastics and steel
Today new joints for the body can be made from plastic or steel.

Heart surgery

Before the Second World War no one operated on hearts. As soon as the chest was cut open, the lungs collapsed. If the heart was touched it stopped.

A US surgeon, Dwight Harken, came across many soldiers with bullets or bits of shrapnel in their hearts. He tried to save them. He cut into the beating heart and hooked out the bullet with his fingers.

The main problem with cutting into the heart was that the blood supply had to be stopped. A surgeon only had four minutes to operate. The brain was damaged if the blood supply was stopped for more than four minutes.

Lower temperatures

A Canadian surgeon, Bill Biggelow came up with a new idea. He lowered the temperature of the patient's body. This slowed the body down. It meant that the surgeon now had more time to operate once he had cut open the heart.

▼ A surgeon using an endoscope to look inside the patient. It is inserted through a small incision in the patient's abdomen. The camera on the end of the endoscope sends images to the monitor.

Source N

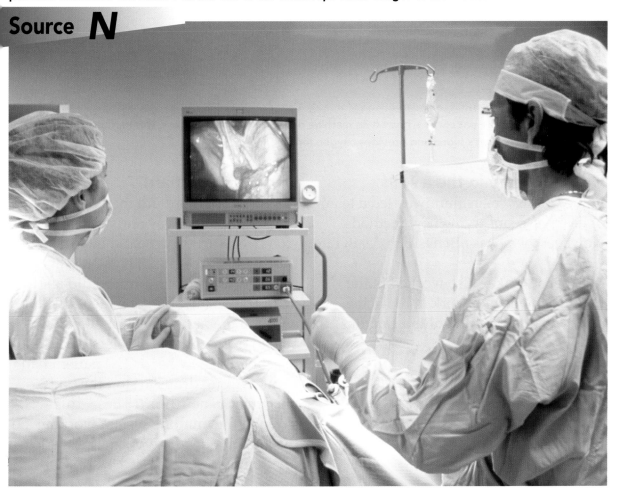

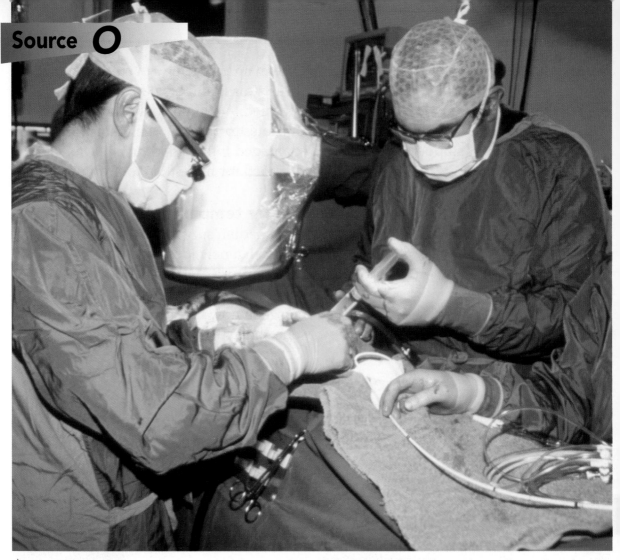

▲ Surgeons attaching a patient to a heart-lung machine during heart valve surgery. This machine takes over the circulation of the patient's blood and provides oxygen for the blood.

Heart Surgery in the 1960s

In the USA Norman Shumway led a team of heart surgeons trying new methods. However there was often a high death rate.

Michael de Blakey also worked in the USA. He pioneered work in replacing diseased arteries with knitted Dacron.

Heart transplants

Many surgeons wanted to be able to transplant a healthy heart (perhaps from someone killed in a road accident) to replace a sick heart. However, the body usually rejected the new heart.

Christiaan Barnard

Christiaan Barnard did the first heart transplant. Shumway and another American surgeon also did heart transplants. At first patients only lived for a few days. Then Barnard did another heart transplant and the patient lived for a year and a half. However, no one was able to overcome the problem of the body rejecting the new heart. The patient had to take strong drugs to stop the body rejecting the new heart. These drugs stopped the immune system working. So the patient often died of an illness such as pneumonia.

CHRISTIAAN BARNARD
Pioneering surgeon

Born: South Africa.

Career: Studied at Cape Town University. Went to the USA to study heart treatment in the 1950s.

In 1967 he transplanted the heart of a road accident victim into a 59 year old man. The man lived for 18 days. Barnard became world famous. He was surprised by all the publicity.

Died: 2001.

Failure

The failure rate was too high. Heart transplant operations were stopped. Some doctors tried artificial hearts. In 1982, one man was given a plastic heart. He died three weeks later.

A new breakthrough – Cyclosporin

By chance someone discovered a new antibiotic in 1974, It stopped antibodies attacking a new heart but it did not kill off all the antibodies. Transplants were possible again. By 1987, 90 per cent of patients with transplants lived for two years or more. Transplants are now done regularly.

Source P

Tiny tubes, wires, balloons, coils, glue and plastic particles are the new tools. The chances are that soon your doctor will be threading a few of these tools into your blood vessels or through the skin into one of your organs. The treatment will be done guided by powerful imaging machines, like ultra scanners, X-ray and computerised tomography.

▲ Adapted from writings by a US doctor.

Source Q

150 years ago patients only had operations if they were desperate. Now with modern anaesthesia, with antiseptics, with blood transfusions, with antibiotics, everything from the brain to bunions is there for the surgeon's healing knife.

▲ Adapted from a comment made by Professor Harold Ellis in a BBC TV programme.

Hospital administrators said we were spending too much. They had the stupidity to say that if we kept patients out we could save money. I said. 'No problem. We've got a shot gun. You fire it because that's what you're planning.'

▲ **Adapted from words spoken by a heart surgeon in the 1960s.**

SUMMARY

▶ The combination of anaesthetics and antiseptics, developed by Joseph Lister, meant that surgery became much safer after 1870.

▶ Aseptic surgery, when no germs are ever allowed to be present, soon replaced antiseptic surgery.

▶ The discovery of the different blood groups allowed safe transfusions thus reducing the risks from blood loss in surgery.

▶ Surgeons began to specialize as surgery became safer. Plastic surgery, brain and heart surgery were developed by individuals.

▶ Developments in science and technology contributed to new techniques in medicine.

▶ The wars fought in the 20th century speeded up developments in surgery.

High-tech surgery
1 Transplants and cloning
Operations can now be carried out which would only have been dreamt of 30 years ago. Transplants are common. Some scientists dream of the day when they will be able to clone human organs so they can have them ready and waiting for transplant operations.
2 Laser treatment
Lasers are used in minor operations, such as correcting eye faults. They are also used to control some cancers.
3 Surgery for unborn babies
Surgeons can now detect problems in unborn babies. They can then perform operations to correct the faults.

Difficulties for the National Health Service
So much can be done nowadays that the NHS does not have enough money to pay for all the operations that could be done.

There have been cases where treatment for someone with a 'self-imposed illness' perhaps as a result of smoking, has been put further down the list than other operations.

The cost of a heart transplant might mean that several other people could not have smaller, less expensive operations.

QUESTIONS

1 Choose two individuals and write down why they were important in the development of surgery since 1870.

2 Read **Discoveries that have helped surgery since 1895.** How did the heart and lung machine help surgeons?

3 Read Sources Q and R.

   a What are the four discoveries that mean so many people can be helped by surgery?

   b In what way does Source R suggest that things are not as rosy as suggested in Source Q?

4 'It can't be right that some patients are refused treatment.' Explain whether you agree with this.

Nursing before 1850

Many women nursed their families when they were sick. But there was no training for nurses. Paid nurses worked by common sense and what they had learnt from others. Some had a bad reputation for drinking and being dirty.

In the 1850s a German doctor ran a small hospital at Kaiserwerth. He insisted on a good standard of nursing. Elizabeth Fry set up a school for nurses in England after she had visited the hospital at Kaiserwerth.

Florence Nightingale (1820–1910)

Florence Nightingale wanted to be a nurse. It took her seven years to persuade her parents to let her do this. She visited Kaiserwerth and then studied nursing in Paris. In 1853 she ran the Institution for the Care of Sick Gentlewomen in London.

The Crimean War (1854–56)

Britain went to war against Russia in a place called the Crimea. There were many battles. Soldiers were dying in dirty, crowded hospitals at places such as Scutari.

Florence Nightingale at Scutari

The British Secretary for War was a friend of the Nightingale family. He asked if Florence would go out to Scutari. He wanted her to organize the hospital there. Florence sailed for Scutari with 38 nurses she had chosen.

The army doctors did not like all these female nurses arriving. But Nightingale was a good organizer. She obtained better water supplies and better food. She made sure that the wards were kept clean and that there were plenty of bandages. The death rate dropped from 42 per cent to 2 per cent.

Source S

▲ This illustration shows how nurses were pictured in the first half of the 19th century – old, ugly and probably drunk.

Source T

She was a woman of iron will. She had friends in the government. She was determined to improve nursing education and care. She succeeded.

The organization of medical and nursing services everywhere, owe something to her spirit.

▲ Adapted from Philip Rhodes, *An Outline History of Medicine*, 1985.

Source U

Mary Seacole was a wonderful woman ...All the men asked her advice and used her herbal medicines rather than report to the doctors. She always helped the wounded after a battle and this made her loved by the whole army.

▲ From the memories of a British soldier who fought in the Crimean War.

Mary Seacole (1805–81)

Mary Seacole was born in Jamaica. Her mother ran a home for sick soldiers. Mary helped her mother look after the patients.

The Crimean War

Seacole went to Britain and asked to go out to the Crimea as a nurse. She was rejected. She did not give up. She sailed for the Crimea (paying for her own ticket).

She set up a medical store, and looked after soldiers on the battlefield too. Seacole met Florence Nightingale, who would not take her on as a nurse.

After the Crimean War

Mary Seacole went back to Britain but no one thanked her for the work she had done. She went bankrupt.

Then the newspapers took up her story. Some money was raised to help her and she wrote her life story to raise money too.

Source V

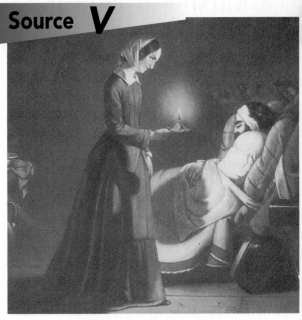

▲ Florence Nightingale became known as 'the lady with the lamp'. This picture was painted by Tomkins in 1855.

Source W

▲ A picture of Mary Seacole from her autobiography, *The Wonderful Adventures of Mrs Seacole*, 1857.

▲ The hospital at Scutari, after it had been cleaned and reorganized by Nightingale nurses.

The rise of nursing

On her return to England Florence Nightingale became very famous. She wrote a book called *Notes on Nursing*, describing her method of nursing. Nightingale wanted to train more women as nurses. A lot of money was raised for her.

The money was used to set up the Nightingale School of Nursing at St Thomas's Hospital in London.

Good nursing

Florence Nightingale said that hospitals must be kept clean and nurses must work very hard and be well trained. Each nurse trained for three years.

Very soon other training schools were set up. By 1900 there were 64,000 trained nurses in Britain.

In 1919 the government passed an Act which laid down qualifications needed to become a nurse.

QUESTIONS

1 In what ways were Florence Nightingale and Mary Seacole:

a the same

b different?

2 a Which woman did more to set up nursing as a job?

b Why do you think this was?

3 What did the government do in 1919?

150 years ago men did not allow women to go to university. In 1849 an American woman, born in Britain, became a doctor in New York. Her name was Elizabeth Blackwell. However, in Britain male doctors were very much against women doctors. They said women were 'too emotional' to become doctors.

Things begin to change

In the 1860s some people began to say that women should have the same rights as men.

The first women doctors

Elizabeth Garrett Anderson and Sophia Jex-Blake were the first women to qualify as doctors in Britain. Women worked in the medical services in both First and Second World Wars.

The Sex Discrimination Act 1975

Through the 20th century more and more women trained as doctors. Then, in 1975, a law was passed in Parliament. It said that all jobs were open to women and men on the same terms.

Source Y

Women are being held back in the race to become senior hospital doctors because of the 'working all hours' culture that remains in the NHS.

▲ From a newspaper of 27 June 2001. It explains that women with families find the long hours difficult.

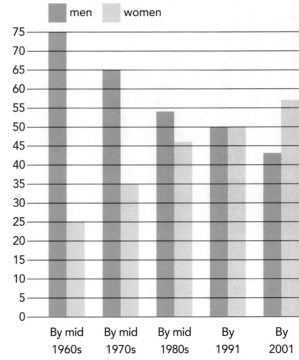

▲ The percentage proportion of women and men in medical schools in Britain.

QUESTIONS

1 What changed in the 1860s that helped women to become doctors?
2 Look at the graph. In which year were there the same number of men and women in medical schools in Britain?
3 Read Source Y. Why can't women get the top jobs in hospitals?

ELIZABETH BLACKWELL:
The first woman doctor

Born: Bristol 1821

Career: Elizabeth's family emigrated to the USA. Elizabeth wanted to become a doctor. She taught herself enough science to be able to study medicine. However, 29 medical schools refused her because she was a woman. She was accepted by a college in New York State. In 1849 she graduated top of her class.

She set up a clinic for children in New York in 1853. In 1859 she travelled to Europe. She met Elizabeth Garrett Anderson and inspired her to become a doctor.

Died: 1910.

ELIZABETH GARRETT ANDERSON
(1836–1917)

Born: London 1836

Education: Her father was a rich merchant so she had a good education. She met Elizabeth Blackwell in 1859 and was inspired to become a doctor. She applied to every medical school between 1861 and 1865. She was refused because she was a woman.

Career: Elizabeth trained as a nurse at Middlesex Hospital. She then went to lectures for male student doctors. They complained and she was forbidden to attend.

In the end she trained privately. In 1865 she passed the examinations of the Society of Apothecaries. She was a doctor. She soon had a big practice in London. She followed this with a French degree in medicine.

In 1882 she opened the New Hospital for Women in London. In 1883 she became Dean of the London School of Medicine for Women.

Died: 1917.

SOPHIA JEX-BLAKE
(1840–1912)

Born: Hastings 1840

Education: Sophia was the daughter of a doctor. He did not want her to go to university but gave in. She later toured Europe and the USA teaching mathematics.

Career: In 1869 she persuaded Edinburgh University to allow her and three other women to study medicine. They had separate classes from the men. But the men complained. Sophia took the University to court. But she lost the case. She took the case to Parliament. In 1875 a law was passed making it legal to award degrees to women. Meanwhile Sophia had trained in Switzerland.

She founded the London School of Medicine for Women in 1874.

Died: 1912.

12.6 Exercise – anaesthetics and anticeptics

▲ 'Operation Madness', a cartoon from the 1870s.

Source 2

Anaesthetics meant surgeons were free to try operations which before had been beyond them. The risk of infection was increased.

▲ Richard Shryock, *The Development of Modern Medicine* 1948.

Source 3

I fill the abdomen with warm water and wash all the organs. The water is plain unfiltered tap water and has not been boiled.

▲ Said by a well known surgeon in 1882. He did not believe in using antiseptics.

1 Look at Source 1.

   a Is the cartoon saying that operations are very safe, not very safe, or just that surgeons are doing lots more operations? Explain your answer.

   b Do you think it gives you reliable evidence about anaesthetics?

2 Read Source 2.
   Why were anaesthetics and antiseptics both needed to make complicated operations safe?

3 Was everyone using antiseptics by 1882? Which source helps you to answer this question.

12.6 Exercise – nursing in the 19th century

Background information
After 1850 the training of nurses changed. Florence Nightingale was given the credit for the changes. Some of the changes were also due to Mary Seacole.

Source 1

Nurses are like housemaids. They do not need much training. They need to know how to make a poultice, how to clean and how to look after patients. The new hospital nurse training scheme is not supported by the doctors.

▲ Adapted from comments by the President of the Royal College of Surgeons in 1851. He was commenting on an idea of setting up a training school for nurses.

Source 2

They are unfitted for the hard work and heavy responsibilities of medical and surgical practice. Women might become midwives. I know of no great discoveries in science by women. What right have women to claim mental equality to men?

▲ Adapted from an article about the role of women in medicine. It was written by a male doctor.

Source 3

You are expected to become skilful:

1 In dressing blisters, sores, wounds and putting on poultices and dressings.

2 In putting on leeches, externally and internally.

3 In looking after helpless patients, keeping them clean etc.

4 In attending operations.

5 In cooking for the sick.

▲ From instructions for trainee nurses at Florence Nightingale's School for Nurses at St Thomas's Hospital in 1862.

1 Read Source 1. The writer is a top doctor. Does this mean that a historian studying the history of medicine should pay particular attention to what he says? Explain your answer.

2 Read Source 2.
   a What does the writer think women might become?
   b What does this source tell you about attitudes in medicine in 1870?

3 Look at Source V on page 116. How reliable do you think this source is as evidence of Florence Nightingale's work in the Crimea? Explain your answer.

CHAPTER 13

DEVELOPMENTS IN PUBLIC HEALTH

13.1 Public health in Britain before 1700

Before the Romans
Before the Romans came to Britain the people of Britain lived in small tribal groups. They were not savages but they did not live like the Romans. They did not often wash. They did not worry about how they got rid of rubbish and sewage.

Roman Britain
The Romans were very practical. When they occupied Britain, they brought their ideas about keeping clean and sewage disposal with them.

Roman towns
Roman towns had public baths, sewers, clean piped water, toilets and drains for everyone to use.

Roman villas
Roman villas were in the country. These villas had baths, piped water, toilets, drains and sewers too. The villas might be occupied by Romans or by Britons who had adopted Roman ways.

End of the empire
From AD 44 the Roman army pulled out of Britain. Britain was on the edge of the Roman Empire. It was one of the first places to be abandoned by the Romans. After the Romans had gone, most of the changes they had brought were lost.

The Middle Ages, AD 1000–1450
In the Middle Ages there was no piped water or drainage in towns. The towns were very dirty even though some people did think that dirt caused 'bad air' and maybe disease.

Most of the time sewage and rubbish piled up in the streets. The other common place for disposing of sewage and rubbish was the river. This was the same river that people got water from for cooking. The filth in the streets and rivers meant that disease spread easily.

Source A

The latrine outside the city walls is badly maintained. Many sicknesses arise from the horrible infected atmosphere coming from this latrine.

▲ This complaint was made in 1415 so the latrines were pulled down. They were rebuilt over a stream called Walbrook that flowed into the River Thames.

▼ In the Middle Ages people often built toilets out over the street or between buildings like this one.

Source B

Early Modern period 1450–1700

Towns grew quickly. London's population rose from about 60,000 in 1520 to about 200,000 in 1603. Other cities grew too. More people meant more waste of all kinds. There were still no drains or piped water.

The cost

Cleaning up waste, providing piped water and sewer pipes all cost money. It was hard for any group of people or town corporation to raise the money for a big job like putting in sewers.

Plague again

The filth, especially in the cities, led to outbreaks of the Black Death or plague. In 1665 there was a very bad outbreak.

Source D

▲ An engraving of people burying plague victims at Holy Well Mount, London, in 1665.

Source E

If there is plague in a house, the house, and the people in it, must be shut up for a month after the last death there. The streets are to be kept clean.

▲ Some of the laws passed in London in 1665 to try to stop the plague from spreading.

Source C

Their rooms are planned so that there is no through draught. (Galen recommended a through draught in a room). Floors are spread with clay and then with rushes. New rushes are put on top of the old ones. The layers become full of old vomit, urine, spittle and cast off food. This causes bad air which is bad for health.

▲ Adapted from a letter about English houses written in 1524 by a Dutchman who was living in England.

QUESTIONS

1 Read **Before the Romans**. What did the Britons do about washing and getting rid of rubbish and sewage?
2 Read **Roman towns** and **Roman villas**. What did Roman towns and villas have?
3 Read **The Middle Ages** and Source C. What connection did some people make in the Middle Ages and the Early Modern period between dirt and disease?
4 Read **Early Modern period** and **The cost**. Why did no one clean up the towns and put in sewers?
5 Look at Sources D and E. Write down the precautions taken against the plague. Now look back at Source W on page 57. Are there any differences between the precautions then and the precautions in 1665?

Towns get bigger

From the late-18th century, more and more people were born and survived childhood diseases. Many of them went to work in the new factories. This meant that more houses were built around factories, so towns grew bigger and bigger.

The houses were crowded together. There were no pipes to take the sewage away. Many of the towns were filthy.

Smoke from factories

The new factories made woollen cloth, cotton, iron machinery and so on. They used coal to make power to run the machines. Smoke and fumes belched out of the chimneys. The government did nothing to improve the living conditions in the towns. They were very unhealthy places indeed.

THE GROWTH OF TOWNS 1801–1901 (in thousands)			
City	1801	1851	1901
Birmingham	71	233	523
Bradford	13	104	280
Leeds	53	172	429
Liverpool	82	376	704
Manchester	70	303	645
Newcastle	33	88	247
Nottingham	29	57	240
Sheffield	46	135	407

Source F

Alfred Row and Beckwith Row are surrounded by an open drain. The houses have common, open privies [toilets] which are in the most offensive condition.

In one house I found six persons living in a very small room, two in a bed, ill with fever.

In the same room a woman was working as a silk weaver.

▲ Two streets in Bethnal Green, London, described by Dr Thomas Southwood-Smith in 1838.

▼ Manchester in about 1854.

Source G

Dirt and disease

Where there was dirt there was disease. **Typhoid** was spread by dirty water. Typhus was spread by the bites from body lice.

Dirty living and poor food meant that people were less strong. They easily caught other diseases like smallpox and tuberculosis.

Cholera

In 1831 a new disease reached Britain. It was called **cholera**. So many people died that the government gave orders about burying people quickly.

By the end of 1832, cholera had spread over most of the country. About 21,000 people had died. Then the disease seemed to die out. But it came back again in 1848, 1854 and 1866.

The cause of cholera

No one knew what caused cholera at the time. Some people thought it was spread by poisonous gases in the air. Barrels of tar were burnt in the streets to try and purify the air.

Now we know it was caused by a germ. This germ attacks the intestines. The sick person gets diarrhoea, vomiting, fever and soon dies.

Cholera is spread through water that is infected by the sewage from people with cholera.

Source H

▲ Washing the dirty bedclothes of someone who had cholera, 1832. The stream was where most people got their drinking water.

Source I

Families huddled together in dirty rooms. There are slaughter houses in Butcher Row with rotting heaps of Offal. Lots of pigs are kept. Chickens are kept in cellars. There are dung heaps everywhere.

▲ From *The History of the Cholera in Exeter in 1832* written by Dr Thomas Shapter in 1842.

Source J

▶ A memorial to 420 cholera victims in Dumfries, Scotland, 1832.

Edwin Chadwick

Everyone was shocked by the cholera epidemic of 1832. Something had to be done.

The government asked Edwin Chadwick to write a report about how poor people lived. The report came out in 1842. It said that many people in Britain were living in filthy and overcrowded houses.

Many people, including the rich, were horrified by Chadwick's report.

Source K

In one part of Market Street there is a dunghill. Yet it is too large to be called a dunghill. It is filth from all over the town. The person who deals in the dung sells it by the cartload.

This place is horrible, with swarms of flies which give a strong taste of the dunghill to any food left uncovered.

▲ This was written by Dr Laurie for Chadwick's report. It is about Greenock in Scotland.

Source L

EDWIN CHADWICK
1800–90

Chadwick was a lawyer.

He began to work for the government in 1832. He wrote a long report on the way poor people lived in Britain. It was called *A Report on the Sanitary Condition of the Labouring Population*. The report showed what terrible conditions many people lived in.

Chadwick said that if the towns were cleaner, there would be less disease. Then people would not need to take time off work.

Chadwick said that Parliament should pass laws to clean up towns. There should be pipes to take sewage away from houses. There should be pipes to bring clean water to houses.

Chadwick's work inspired the sanitory reform movement.

◀ The death of Prince Albert, Queen Victoria's husband. He died of typhoid fever in 1861. Windsor Castle had piped water. But the water was piped from the River Thames, which was filthy.

The Clean Party

After Chadwick's report a lot of people said that towns must be cleaned up.

They said that Parliament must pass a law saying that towns must have clean water for everyone. All the sewage must be taken away.

The Dirty Party

In 1847 a Public Health Bill was read in Parliament. Some people were against it.

They said that it was not the government's job to clean up towns. People should do it for themselves. If the government cleaned up the towns it would cost a lot of money. It would also mean that the government was poking its nose into everyone's business.

This way of thinking was called *laissez-faire* ('leave things alone' in French).

Cholera again 1848

Cholera struck again in 1848. Thousands died in the dirty towns. Suddenly, everyone wanted a clean up. The Public Health Act was made law in 1848.

Chadwick said that diseases such as cholera were caused by the rotting filth in towns. The towns should be cleaned up. The most important things were:

- good drains
- taking away rubbish
- clean water supplies.

'This expense would be a financial gain by lessening the cost of sickness and death.'

▲ The main ideas from Chadwick's Report of 1842.

Those against the Leeds Sewerage Scheme wanted to save the pockets of the ratepayers. Their idea was that the sewers were to discharge into the river nearby, thus carrying on the pollution.

▲ Adapted from *Report on the Condition of the Town of Leeds*, 1844.

The First Public Health Act 1848

Central Board of Health in London to sit for five years.

Local Boards of Health could be set up in towns if 10% of the rate payers agreed. These boards had the power to improve water supply and sewage disposals. They took over from private companies and individuals.

The Act was not compulsory. It was not fully applied across the whole country.

▲ The terms of the first Public Health Act, 1848.

QUESTIONS

1 Towns grew because the Industrial Revolution meant more workers were needed for the factories. How did this affect health?

2 a Edwin Chadwick and the Clean Party wanted to clean up towns. Why?

   b Why did the Dirty Party try to stop them?

   c What changed their minds?

The 1848 Public Health Act

This law said that towns could set up Boards of Health to clean up towns (but they did not have to). So only 182 towns did anything about cleaning up their water supplies and sewage.

Laissez-faire again

Some people still did not want the government to poke its nose into people's houses and streets, however dirty. Some rich people did not want to pay taxes to clean up poor parts of the towns.

Showing how cholera spread

Dr John Snow worked in London near Broad Street. He asked lots of people where they obtained their water. He noticed that all the people who caught cholera took their water from a pump in Broad Street. He took the handle off the pump. No one caught cholera. He showed that cholera was spread by infected water.

Chadwick and doctors

Chadwick said that everyone could be healthy if they had a clean place to live. He did not think much of doctors or hospitals. Some doctors disagreed with him. Sir John Simon, who was made Medical Officer for Health in 1858, said you need a clean place to live and you need a good doctor as well.

The government takes action

By 1872 the government realised that it had to do more about cleaning up towns. An Act of 1872 divided Britain into different areas. Each area had a Medical Officer of Health. A second Public Health Act was passed in 1875. This said that local town councils must provide clean water. In the same year an Act was passed saying that decent houses should be built for the workers. Britain was on its way to becoming a cleaner place.

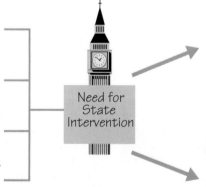

- Further cholera outbreaks in 1854 and 1866 frighten the authorities once more.
- In 1854 Dr John Snow showed that cholera was spread by contaminated water.
- In 1864 Louis Pasteur demonstrated the germ theory of disease. Need for cleanliness became clear.
- By the 1870s statistics showed that poor living conditions and disease were connected.

Need for State Intervention

1875 Second Public Health Act
- brought together all previous laws under one act.
- councils compelled to provide street lighting, clean water, drainage, and sewage disposal.
- councils had to employ medical inspectors.

1875 Artisans' Dwellings Act
- councils given power to buy up areas of slum housing, knock them down and build new houses.
- few councils took advantage.

▲ **Factors leading to state intervention into public health.**

OCTAVIA HILL

Born: 1838.

Her parents and grandparents were involved in charity work, so Octavia and her sisters naturally joined in.

Career: In 1853 Octavia started to work with the poor. She taught in a ragged school. Working in poor areas showed her how appalling the housing conditions of the poor were. She began to plan how they could be improved. In 1865 she managed to raise enough money to buy the leases of three houses. She repaired them, collected the rent regularly and got to know the tenants. She made sure that tenants did not take in lodgers – which led to severe overcrowding and the spread of infection. She got rid of the bad tenants and improved the homes for the remaining tenants, who then looked after the houses.

Soon many people were paying Octavia to manage their properties for them. She used the money she made to buy up more houses for the poor. People began to think that Octavia talked a lot of sense about how to help the poor.

In 1869 she helped to found the Charity Organisation Society to look into living conditions for the poor.

She also worked to make sure that open parks were kept around cities so that everyone could enjoy open space and fresh air.

JOHN SNOW
AND CHOLERA

Born: 1813.

Career: He was apprenticed to a surgeon at the age of 14. In 1838, Snow travelled to London. There he qualified as a member of the Royal College of Surgeons. He set up as a doctor in Soho.

In 1848 cholera broke out in London. Snow discovered that in one place in London the people who caught cholera drank water from a particular pump which brought water from the Thames. The people who did not catch it drank water from fresh springs. He suggested that the disease was transmitted by water.

Source O

The state of the air which encourages cholera is a hot, moist atmosphere. Animal and vegetable refuse rots quickly. The poisons from it are carried into the blood from the lungs.

▲ A report from the new Central Board of Health. It explains why cholera was worse in the summer.

DIPHTHERIA.   SCROFULA.   CHOLERA.

FATHER THAMES INTRODUCING HIS OFFSPRING TO THE FAIR CITY OF LONDON.
(A Design for a Fresco in the New Houses of Parliament.)

▲ **A Punch cartoon of 1858 showing Father Thames introducing his children (diphtheria, scrofula and cholera) to London.**

Source Q

In dry weather the Thames becomes a huge lake. Little of the river reaches the sea. Instead the filth of more than 2 million people collects in this lake. In times of cholera the evacuations of patients join the other filth in the river.

▲ **A description of the River Thames, from the 1850s.**

QUESTIONS

1 Read Source P. How did people catch cholera according to the Central Board of Health?
2 Read **JOHN SNOW and cholera**. How did people catch cholera according to John Snow?
3 'Source Q shows that many people agreed with Snow about catching cholera.' Explain whether you agree with this statement.

Finding out about the poor

Charles Booth investigated how people lived in the East End of London.

He asked a lot of questions and wrote a book called *Life and Labour of the People in London*.

He said that one third of the people lived below the poverty line. These people did not have enough money to eat properly. They lived in bad houses. If they fell ill they could not afford to pay a doctor. People were poor because of sickness, old age, low wages or unemployment.

Seebohm Rowntree asked the same sort of questions in York. He found the same answers as Booth had.

The Boer War 1899–1902

Then came the Boer War. Nearly half the men who wanted to join the army were unfit. They had grown up without enough food to eat. People were shocked.

The work of the Liberals 1906–14

The Liberal government was in power from 1906. They said something must be done to help poor people. One Liberal, Winston Churchill, said that the government had a duty to look after children, the sick and the elderly.

The box show the laws that the Liberal government passed.

▲ Slum housing in the East End of London in 1912.

Date	Legislation
1906	**Provision of school meals** – local authorities given the power to provide free school meals.
1907	**School medical inspections.**
1909	**Old Age Pension Act** – people over 70 to receive 5s [25p] per week state pension as long as their income from other sources was not more than 12s [60p] per week.
1909	**Labour Exchanges** set up to help unemployed find work.
1911	**National Insurance Act** – two parts: Part I: Workers in manual trades earning less than £160 per year to pay 4d [2p] per week. The employer added 3d [1½p] and the government 2d [1p]. Workers entitled to 10s [50p] per week if they were off work sick, for upto 26 weeks. Free medical treatment available from a panel doctor. Part II: Workers, earning less than £160 per year in certain trades, together with the government and employers paid in 2½d [1p] per week. Workers could claim 7s [35p] unemployment pay for up to 15 weeks.

▲ Laws passed by the Liberal government 1906–14.

People against the new laws

Some people did not like the new laws. They said that people should be independent. They should not have old age pensions given to them. Rich people knew that the old age pensions would be paid for out of taxes paid by the better off. The rich did not want to pay more taxes.

In 1911 a National Insurance Act was passed (see box on page 131). This gave money to some workers if they could not work because they were sick or unemployed. Again some people said that workers should be more independent.

David Lloyd George

David Lloyd George was a leading member of the Liberal government. He pushed through many of the laws and said that this was only a start. There was a lot further to go to help poor people.

More laws 1919–39

After the First World War (1914–18) Lloyd George said he would make Britain 'a country fit for heroes to live in'.

In 1919 the Ministry of Health was set up. It was to deal with everything to do with health in Britain.

Also in 1919 a new law was passed to get more houses built for poorer people.

In 1920 another National Insurance Act was passed. The number of workers who were paid money because they were sick or unemployed was increased. Now only farm workers and servants were not covered.

THE GLORIOUS FIFTEENTH

OUR ST. SEBASTIAN. "AND NOW, LADIES AND GENTLEMEN, AFTER THESE REFRESHING PRELIMINARIES, LET US GET TO BUSINESS."

▲ Lots of people were against Lloyd George and his National Insurance Act. Do you think the cartoonist was for or against Lloyd George?

QUESTIONS

1 Look at the diagram on page 128. What factors made the government do more about public health?

2 Look at the box on page 131. Write down the laws about the following:

a children

b health and sickness

c the unemployed

d old people.

3 Why were some people against things like the Old Age Pension Act and the National Insurance Act?

Bad times

Throughout the 1920s and 1930s the government was short of money. But, even so, a Pensions Act was passed in 1925. This said people should receive a pension when they were 65 years old.

Then there was a trade depression in the 1930s. Many people were unemployed. The government had to spend a lot of money on dole payments. There was not enough money left for anything else.

Many people still said that the government must do more about health. While the government (local authorities) did do some things about health, other things were done by volunteers. The whole set up was a muddle. For instance, the government provided 2000 hospitals but there were also another 1000 hospitals paid for by voluntary funds (see diagram below).

The Second World War broke out in 1939. It changed people's attitudes towards health care.

▲ This cartoon shows a member of the government wanting to lead the way to more laws about health.

An unco-ordinated system

Hospitals
- About 3000 in Britain, 1000 were run by voluntary funds. Hospitals unevenly spread.
- Poor people were treated in workhouse infirmaries.

Doctors
- Wealthy received best treatment as they could afford the fees.
- Some workers, covered by National Insurance, had panel doctors. [dependants not covered]

Other services
Local authorities provided:
- school medical inspectors
- ante-natal clinics
- infant-welfare centres.

▲ Health care in 1939.

Source U

In 1939 most workers [but not their wives or children] were covered by social insurance schemes.

There were state schools and hospitals. There were ante-natal clinics and infant welfare clinics. Three million children got free milk in school.

▲ Paul Addison, *A New Jerusalem*, 1994.

In the early part of the 20th century there had been some reforms. These were to improve the way poorer people lived and worked. One of these was the Old Age Pensions Act in 1908.

In the 1920s and 1930s there was help with housing and unemployment benefit.

All these things were steps on the way to the government looking after everyone.

The Second World War

The Second World War broke out in Europe in 1939. The government had to do a lot of things to help win the war. Some of these things helped to change the way people lived.

- During the war there was not much food. The government made sure children had enough food. Free milk was given out at school. More children had free school meals.
- Britain was bombed heavily during the war. Many people were injured. All hospitals came under government control (the Ministry of Health). There was free treatment. People began to think this was a good thing.
- Thousands of children were evacuated from the cities to get them away from the bombing. They were sent to live with people in the country. Many of these country people were shocked at the filthy, badly clothed state of many city children. This led to lots of people saying something should be done about improving living conditions for the poor.

Source V

◀ A cartoon from the *Daily Mirror* published during the Second World War. It shows 'War' providing food and vitamins to a young child.

Source W

We have never seen so many children with lice and nits. It seemed as if they hadn't bathed for months. Some children had dirty sores all over their bodies. Many of the children were bedwetters.

▲ Adapted from a report of the Women's Institute in 1940.

The Beveridge Report 1942

William Beveridge wanted a Welfare State where the government helped people 'from the cradle to the grave'. In 1942 he published *The Beveridge Report*. In it he said he wanted everyone to be free from the five 'giants'. These were the following:

- Want (not enough money to live a healthy life).
- Disease.
- Ignorance (everyone to have a chance to go to school).
- Squalor (filthy houses).
- Idleness (no work).

The Beveridge Report became a best seller. People wanted a better life for everyone after the war. Only people like Winston Churchill asked how it was to be paid for.

The Labour government 1945–51

In July 1945 the Labour government came to power. They passed many laws to help poor people. The most important was the setting up of the National Health Service (NHS).

The National Health Service

The National Health Service started in 1948. It was the idea of Aneurin Bevan. It provided lots of things for free, including the following:

- hospitals
- doctors and dentists
- opticians
- ambulances
- vaccinations
- health visitors and maternity clinics.

Some doctors did not want to work for the government. So as well as being paid a fee (by the government) for each patient, they were allowed to treat private patients too.

Source **X**

▲ A cartoon published in the *Evening Standard* in December 1949. It is called 'Right Turn'.

SIR WILLIAM BEVERIDGE

Born: 1879.

Education: He was educated at Oxford University.

Career: In 1919 he became the Director of the London School of Economics. In 1942 he wrote the famous Beveridge Report. Two years later he became a Liberal MP in Parliament. He is remembered for his part in bringing about the Welfare State.

What people thought about the NHS

Most people liked the NHS. But there were also many people who were against it.

This is what doctors thought:
For the NHS   4734
Against the NHS   40,814

The things that doctors did not like about it included the following:
- They would be told where to practice.
- They could not charge for their services.
- They would be on a fixed salary.

Aneurin Bevan and the doctors

Aneurin Bevan was the Minister of Health. He had many discussions with the leader of the British Medical Association. In the end, Bevan won the doctors over. He said they would be given a fee for each patient they registered. They would also still be able to treat private (fee paying) patients.

By June 1948, 92 per cent of doctors and most hospitals had agreed to work under the NHS.

Source Y

She went to have her eyes tested, and got some new glasses. Then she went to the chiropodist to have her feet checked. She went to the doctor's because she had trouble with her ears. The doctor said he would get her a hearing aid.

▲ How one old lady reacted to the NHS

The NHS started. My mother and dad had problems with their teeth and I think they were the first to go to the dentist. And instead of having just a few teeth out they had the complete set. And free dentures. They thought it was wonderful.

▲ A woman describing her reaction to the NHS.

QUESTIONS

1 Look at the cartoon.
   Do you think the cartoonist approved or disapproved of the NHS? Explain your answer.

ANUERIN BEVAN

Born: 1897 in Wales.

Career: He worked in the coal mines. Later he became Labour MP for Ebbw Vale.

He became Minister for Health in 1945. He introduced the National Health Service. In a speech to the House of Commons in 1946, he said, 'Worry about money in a time of sickness hinders recovery and is cruel. A satisfactory health service is one that treats rich and poor alike'.

In 1951 the government increased the taxes people pay to pay for the NHS and the Korean War. It also brought in charges for prescriptions. Bevan was so angry that he resigned from the government.

Source Z

▲ A cartoon from 1948 showing Aneurin Bevan dishing out 'NHS medicine' to the doctors.

How the NHS was meant to work
- It aimed to provide the best care for everyone.
- It was to be paid for out of peoples' taxes and National Insurance contributions.

Problems faced by the NHS
- More people lived longer so there were more people to treat.
- New cures were found. Some were very costly, such as transplant operations and many new drugs.
- New illnesses developed such as AIDS.

Spending on the NHS 1950–2002

UK £billion

Year	UK £billion
1950	9.5
1960	11.5
1970	17.0
1980	26.0
1990	34.5
2000	50.0
2002	65.4

How to pay for the NHS
One way of paying for the NHS is to raise prescription charges. Another way is to encourage more people to take out private health insurance.

Some people say that this is against the whole idea of the National Health Service. Others say 'where is the money going to come from?'

Shortage of money
Sometimes patients have to wait so long for important operations they die. Sometimes treatment is refused because of lack of money or because a treatment (such as a heart transplant) will have more chance of success if done for a non-smoker than a smoker.

The Labour government 1997
The Labour government has worked to improve the NHS. Here are things they have done.
- Transferred patients to other countries to have operations, rather than wait a long time in Britain.
- Increased National Insurance contributions.

Vaccination
After 1948 the government paid for the vaccination of all children. Polio was a dreaded disease. It usually struck young people and could paralyse them for life. Jonas Salk found a vaccine for in 1954. The government paid for this too.

World Health Organization
This was set up in 1948. It was to help everyone in the world to be healthier. One of the things it did was to get more children vaccinated. Today eight out of ten children have been vaccinated against the worst diseases.

Doubts
Some doctors have had doubts about the safety of certain vaccines. For instance there is a 'three-in-one' vaccination against mumps, measles and rubella. Some people argue that this has caused **autism** in a number of children. Parents have been worried so the numbers of children being vaccinated have dropped. Other doctors argue that this will lead to an increase in mumps, measles and rubella. This could be serious.

Keeping well

For the last 150 years one type of medicine has dominated in the West. This seems successful. But recently some people have begun to worry that some of the powerful drugs can harm the body. Also our bodies can become immune to some drugs so we have to find new and more powerful ones.

Some people are more interested in other ways to keep healthy (rather than wait until they fall sick). Some people do exercises such as Yoga or take up moderate exercise such as swimming and walking, to keep their bodies working well. They also eat sensibly.

Alternative medicine

Sometimes a person may get lots of colds or headaches or often get aches and pains. Some people have begun to wonder whether it would be better to look at the general health of the patient as a whole rather than give them a pill to make the pain go away. This is an alternative way of looking at health, so it is called alternative medicine. There are several alternatives:

- Herbal medicine. Using herbs is a tried and tested form of medicine used for thousands of years. (Often it is best to go to see a well trained herbalist than to make guesses in a health shop).
- Homeopathy. This is based on the theory that 'like cures like'. A dilute substance of the original illness is given. It rebalances the body.
- Acupuncture. This is based on the flow of life energy (called qi) around the body (rather like an electric circuit going round the body). Sometimes it gets blocked or damaged. Then we are ill or in pain. Metal needles inserted at any of several hundred points on the body make the qi flow better. We then feel better.

Other alternative approaches are shown in the graph.

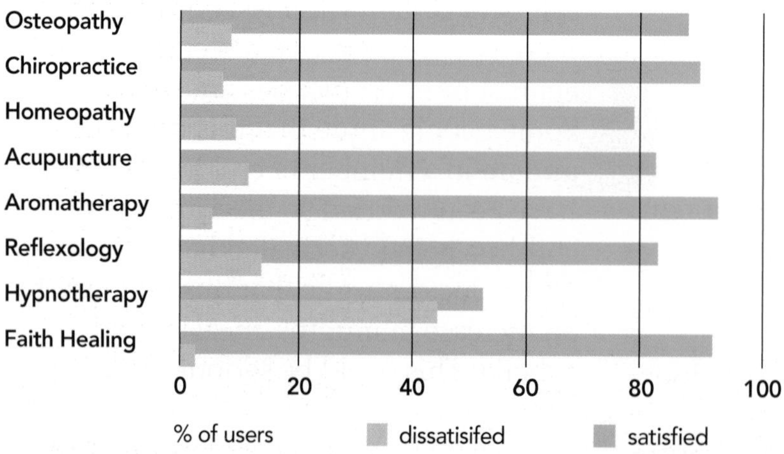

% of users   dissatisifed   satisfied

▲ The results of a recent survey by the consumer magazine, *Which?* It shows that people who had tried alternative treatments mainly regarded them as successful.

QUESTIONS

1 Write out the five giants that Beveridge wanted everyone to be free from.

2 'Doctors were against the NHS in 1948 because they were selfish.' Explain whether you agree with this statement.

3 Look at the graph.

   a List three types of alternative medicine.

   b Write down the four most popular types of alternative medicine.

Source 1

▲ Barrels of tar in the streets of Exeter to stop cholera, 1831–2. Some people thought it was caused by bad air.

1 a Why was burning tar (Source 1) of no use in getting rid of cholera?

  b Why did people do it?

2 Why were there four outbreaks of cholera between 1831 and 1866?

3 Study Source 3. Which event did the most to bring about a Welfare State in Britain. Explain your answer.

Source 2

▲ A view of industrial Sheffield in the mid–19th century.

Source 3

Some events which improved health and welfare in Britain:

1875 Second Public Health Act passed. Local councils were made to provide fresh water and sanitation.

1909 The first Old Age Pensions were paid.

1942 *The Beveridge Report* said that the government should look after its citizens 'from the cradle to the grave'.

1948 The National Health Service came into being – free medical care for everyone.

▲ From a modern history book.

CHAPTER 14

CONCLUSION: CHANGE, CONCEPTS AND FACTORS

The history of medicine is not one of steady progress. At some times change was rapid. At other times change was slow. Sometimes things changed for the worse. Sometimes they changed for the better.

We have only looked at a part of medicine in the world. For instance, more people in the world use traditional Chinese medicine than any other medicine but there is not space for everything.

These are the aspects we have looked at:
- the cause and cure of disease
- anatomy
- surgery
- public health (preventing disease)
- surgeons, doctors and nurses.

These different aspects of medicine have developed at different rates. For example, public health in Britain was better under the Romans than at any time until about 1850. But the understanding of the cause and cure of disease was better from the 1500s than it was in Roman times.

The rise and fall of understanding the cause and cure of disease can be summarised as follows:
1 Good progress in Greece at the time of Hippocrates.
2 Slow progress to the end of the Roman Empire.
3 Sharp fall in the Dark Ages.
4 Slow progress in the Middle Ages (some medical schools).
5 Fast progress during the Renaissance.
6 Slow progress until the 1800s and the germ theory.
7 Fast progress in the 20th century.

The history of medicine gives you a lot of information. The factors and concepts you have used are the tools to shape this information into patterns.

The most important concepts are:
- development and change
- progress and regress
- the rate of change
- trends and turning points.

Find examples of these concepts from the three main periods you have studied:
- Ancient (to the fall of the Roman empire)
- 500 AD–1800 AD
- Modern (from 1800 onwards).

A whole range of factors work with each concept. These include the following:

- *Chance.* Chance can be an important factor in progress. By chance, Paré ran out of boiling oil to use on gunshot wounds in 1537. He was forced to try a new treatment. It was much better. This was progress.
- *War.* War can affect the rate of change. It can speed it up. During the Second World War drug companies put all their efforts into mass producing penicillin. War can also slow down the rate of change. The collapse of the Roman empire followed bitter wars.
- *Religion.* Religion can bring progress and regress. Egyptian religion brought progress due to the mummification of dead bodies. This helped the understanding of anatomy. In the Middle Ages, religion brought regress. The Church forbade the boiling of dead bodies to produce skeletons. This led to a poor knowledge of anatomy.

You may be asked in your exam to give examples of how factors helped or hindered progress. Be prepared! Here are four more factors. Make sure you know about them. They are:
- science and technology
- communications
- the work of individuals
- government.

GLOSSARY

anaesthetics drugs given to a patient to make surgery pain free.

anatomy the structure of the human body.

anthrax a bacterial infection which affects humans and cattle, causing sores on the skin.

antibiotic a drug made from a living organism, such as fungi, which kills bacteria and prevents it from growing.

antibody a defensive substance produced in the body to kill germs or poison.

antiseptic a substance which kills germs.

aqueduct a channel for carrying water.

archaeologist someone who studies history by examining objects found in the earth.

astronomy the study of stars, planets and other objects in space.

autism a condition that causes people to withdraw into a private world and makes it very difficult for them to communicate with others.

blood transfusion taking the blood from one person and putting it into another.

cautery a method of treating amputated limbs or wounds by burning them with hot iron or oil to stop infection and seal the wound.

cesspit a hole which drains empty into.

cholera a bacterial disease, spread by contaminated water, which causes severe vomiting and diarrhoea.

circulating going round; Harvey's understanding of blood circulation was very important to medical development.

clinical observation watching a sick person to monitor and treat their illnesses.

clone to make an exact copy of cells or an organism. In recent years scientists have been able to clone animals such as sheep.

continuity staying the same.

cyst a small lump of diseased body tissue.

dislocated out of position.

dissection cutting a body open to examine the insides.

distillation changing liquid into gas by heating it, and then condensing it again into droplets. This is done to purify liquid or to extract something from it.

embalm preserve a dead body by treating it with chemicals.

empire a group of countries ruled by one other country.

epidemic a breakout of a disease or virus which affects many people.

hygiene health through cleanliness.

inoculation treating someone with a mild dose of a disease or virus to prevent them catching more harmful diseases or viruses.

laxative medicine which makes people go to the toilet to empty their bowels.

leprosy an infectious disease of the skin which can lead to deformities.

miasma bad air, thought to cause diseases.

midwife a person trained to help women give birth.

oath a formal promise.

ointment a medicated cream that is applied to the skin.

opium a drug made from white poppies which makes people sleepy, numb, happy and forgetful.

organs parts of the human body, such as the lungs, heart, brain, kidney and liver.

phlegm thick mucus found in the throat, nose and lungs.

pilgrimage a journey to a shrine or holy place.

plague there are two main forms of plague: bubonic (where people suffer from buboes or lumps), spread by flea bites; and pneumonic (which affects people's lungs), spread by coughing or sneezing.

quack doctor someone who pretends to be a real and qualified doctor but is not.

rational ruled by reason.

scrofula an infectious disease which causes large sores, especially around the neck.

solid cultures experimentally grown bacteria in nutritive solid substances.

supernatural outside the world as we know it, sometimes involving gods, spirits and unknown forces.

symptom how disease or illness affects the body.

tracheotomy an operation which involves cutting into the trachea or windpipe to help people breathe.

tuberculosis a bacterial disease which affects the lungs.

typhoid a bacterial disease, spread by contaminated food and water, which affects the intestines.

vaccination treating someone with a mild dose of disease to prevent them catching more harmful diseases.

INDEX